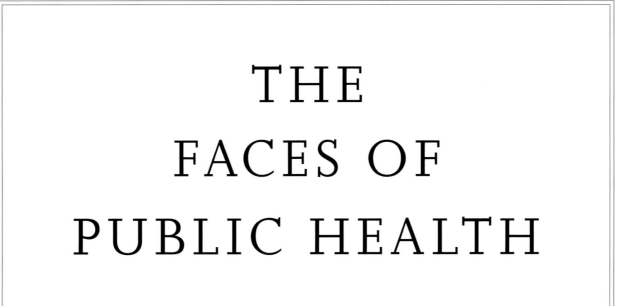

THE
FACES OF
PUBLIC HEALTH

The Faces of Public Health is published by Pfizer Global
Pharmaceuticals, Pfizer Inc, New York, NY copyright ©2004.
All rights reserved. The contents do not necessarily reflect
the views of Pfizer Inc. No part of this publication may be
reproduced in any form without prior written permission
from the publisher. Correspondence should be addressed
to The Faces of Public Health, c/o Senior Medical Director/Group
Leader, Public Health, Pfizer Inc, 235 East 42nd Street,
New York, NY 10017-5755.

ISBN 0-9761815-0-9

Printed in Canada

The Faces of Public Health

Contents

Acknowledgements

Special appreciation goes to the many individuals who helped bring *The Faces of Public Health* to life. We could not have chosen the 25 people profiled in this book without the input of public health officials and professionals across the United States and its territories who took the time to nominate those who, in their opinions, best represent our field. Thanks must also go to the teams who helped develop and produce this book: Dilia Santana and Oscar Perdomo, U.S. Public Health, Pfizer Inc; Ana Rita Velazquez, ScD and Sydney Ann Neuhaus of Fleishman-Hillard International Communications; David L. Farren; and Matt Warhaftig of Warhaftig Associates.

A special debt of gratitude goes to Hugh Tilson, MD, DrPH, Senior Advisor to the Dean and Clinical Professor, School of Public Health, University of North Carolina at Chapel Hill. A longtime friend and tireless advocate for increased awareness of the field of public health, Hugh provided invaluable advice and important editorial contributions throughout the development of the book.

Barbara A. DeBuono, MD, MPH
September 2004

Foreword

The impact of public health is everywhere — in the clean, fluoridated water we drink, in the pasteurized milk our children drink, in the seat belts we buckle, in the smokeless air we breathe as we work in safe indoor environments, and in the competent and accessible health services we receive. Although public health impacts every individual every day, the work of public health can be mysterious to the general public. To celebrate the work of the public health community and to put a face on the thousands of individuals who have committed their lives to the safety and health of our society, Pfizer is pleased to publish *The Faces of Public Health*. This book is a tribute to the more than 400,000 people who work in public health in the United States. We hope it will be a source of inspiration to future generations of public health workers.

Too often public health professionals on the front line do their vital and necessary work in ways that are invisible to the general public. An irony of public health is that when it works well, keeping the population free of diseases and injuries, we don't see it. We take for granted the training and expertise that led to the good work of many public health specialties — biostatistics, chronic disease prevention, epidemiology, infectious disease surveillance, maternal and child health, mental health, occupational health and oral health among them. We also take for granted the hard-won partnerships and collaborations forged across the health care and environmental spectrum that work together to prevent disease and injury. Prevention works well only when all

levels of the public health infrastructure collaborate, both in educating the public about proven ways to lead healthier lives and in discovering creative approaches to contain and prevent emerging health threats. *The Faces of Public Health* aims to make visible the invaluable work public health professionals perform day in and day out and to celebrate their contributions to our nation's well-being.

In early 2003, Pfizer asked each state and territorial health department to nominate two to three individuals who exemplify the best of public health — who work indefatigably every day in their communities to make a difference and whose life stories give texture to all levels of the public health infrastructure. The 25 individuals selected for the profiles in this book, from among many nominations received, represent the broad scope of the public health profession and the diversity of our nation's population. We celebrate contributors from the Alaskan tundra to the south coast of Puerto Rico and from New Hampshire to Greater Los Angeles. We celebrate contributors who are biostatisticians, dental hygienists, educators, epidemiologists, legislators, managers, physicians, sanitarians, social workers and surgeons, and those who work in all sorts of settings, from official public health agencies to state legislatures. As part of the public health infrastructure, they all advocate for the right of each citizen to live a safe and healthy life.

In the pages that follow, you will read the life stories of these exemplary public health professionals and see photographs of them in action. We hope their stories ignite the imaginations of generations to come. For those we need to enlist as our supporters and advocates, we hope these stories dispel some of the mystery surrounding public health and show our true value. For those of us in public health who devote our life's work to making lives healthier, we know these stories will bring a thrill of recognition and cement the feeling of satisfaction that motivates us to keep making a difference.

Barbara A. DeBuono, MD, MPH
Senior Medical Director/Group Leader
U.S. Public Health/U.S. Medical
Pfizer Global Pharmaceuticals
Pfizer Inc

Marilyn Adams

Iowa

Ensuring farm safety for children

Unlike many other workplaces, the American farm encompasses the entire family. For many people, farming conjures up images of golden fields of wheat waving in the breeze, cows being milked and kids riding horses. The reality of farming, however, reveals many potential hazards for all members of the farm family. In 1999, farm occupations were second only to truck driving in the number of U.S. fatalities per year — 557 farm-related fatalities compared to 898 for truck drivers. The National Safety Council reported in 1999 that the fatal injury rate for agriculture (22.5 per 100,000) was second only to mining and quarrying (23.1 per 100,000). Children have always played a role in the family farm's production system and are therefore at risk for injury and death. After one farm family experienced this terrible reality firsthand, they committed themselves to improving farm safety for children.

In 1987, Marilyn Adams founded Farm Safety 4 Just Kids (FS4JK). One year earlier in October 1986, Marilyn lost her 11-year-old son Keith when he suffocated in a gravity flow wagon while he was helping his stepfather load the corn harvest into a storage bin. A nonprofit organization, FS4JK works throughout rural America and overseas to prevent other families from having to endure the profound grief Marilyn and her family suffered after losing Keith. FS4JK employs prevention strategies that reflect public health intervention in the fullest sense and reinforce the role farm safety plays in the field of occupational health.

Marilyn Adams was born in Redfield, Iowa, a small farming community in central Iowa west of Des Moines, and grew up with three older brothers and a younger sister on a large farm that grew corn and soybeans and ran a hog operation. She attended local schools until the family moved to a new farm in an adjoining community, where she graduated from Stuart High School. After graduating, she married her high school sweetheart and continued the farming life. She adopted her first child, Kelly, and then gave birth to a daughter, Kimberley, and a son, Keith. In 1982, she married Darrell Adams. Darrell has three grown children of his own – Kandi, Kent and Kraig – and together he and Marilyn have Kailynn, now a junior high school student, as well as 11 grandchildren. Marilyn and Darrell live on an 800-acre farm outside Earlham, Iowa, the northern gateway to Madison County.

While raising her family, Marilyn pursued a number of real-life learning opportunities, always taking advantage of special training courses to improve her skills. Much of her time was spent teaching Sunday school at her church and helping with the youth group. She ran a childcare center in her home when her daughters were young, and then began work for an insurance company in West Des Moines. At the insurance company, she worked her way up to sales, and at the suggestion of the company, helped found the Mothers Against Drunk Driving (MADD) chapter in West Des Moines. She also took a Dale Carnegie course in public speaking. Marilyn always remembers her grandfather's admonition, "Stand up for what you believe in," and takes the farmer's motto to heart every day, "Do everything you can and then some."

But tragedy struck in October 1986, when Marilyn's only son Keith was 11 years old. Keith was anxious to begin contributing to the business of the family farm. On the first full day of the harvest at his stepdad's request, Keith stayed home from school to help. The night before, Marilyn sat up with Keith to go over his responsibilities the next day. She felt uneasy having Keith take the day off from school, but took comfort from knowing that harvests had been this way for generations. A time always came when the young grew into their roles, helping the family business thrive.

Keith's job was to power the tractor that in turn powered the auger, a long, angled corkscrew that fed the corn kernels from a door at the bottom of an angled gravity flow wagon to the top of a large, round aluminum storage bin. He would climb on a strut of the gravity flow wagon and peer in until all the corn was emptied, then climb down and turn off the tractor until the next load appeared. Every half hour, all through the day, Darrell would bring a new wagon full of corn kernels from the fields, having harvested the corn with a combine that separated the kernels from the cobs, leaving stems, husks and the cobs behind.

By midafternoon, after hours of work with time out only for lunch, Keith might have grown antsy and climbed over the wagon rim into the corn, or maybe he fell in. Regardless, he had no way of knowing that the suction caused by the corn being emptied through the wagon's trap door would pull him under and suffocate him. When Darrell returned with the next load and did not see Keith, he had a premonition. He leapt out of the combine's cab and saw Keith's foot through the open trap door of the gravity flow wagon. The flow of corn had slowed to a trickle. Darrell turned off the power and widened the trap door opening as much as he could. The weight of the corn made it impossible for him to pull Keith out. After Keith's body flowed out with the unloading corn, Darrell quickly laid Keith in his pickup truck and rushed him to the nearest doctor's office.

Marilyn had driven that morning into West Des Moines to take a recertification course. She received a telephone call in the afternoon from the doctor's office letting her know that Keith had been airlifted from the small clinic in Earlham to Blank Children's Hospital in Des Moines, and that she should come quickly. Time stopped for her. She hardly recognized Keith's small face – ashen, blue and scarlet in turns – amid the tubes and machines that were working to resuscitate him in the emergency room. Darrell stood nearby, solemn with reddened, tear-flecked eyes. He had been with Keith since those frantic first few moments trying to pull his body from the gravity flow wagon and he held onto every hope that Keith could survive. Keith died at 2:30 in the morning with the family by his side. Ironically, when Marilyn and Darrell arrived home, their grandfather clock had stopped at 2:30.

Marilyn's grief took her into a downward spiral, away from her family and any thoughts of hope. She was fortunate to have an understanding family that gave her time to survive the deep depression that she thought would never end. She later wrote a book about her experience, *Rhythm of the Seasons: A Journey Beyond Loss*, to help others cope with profound loss. Dr. C. Everett Koop, former U.S. Surgeon General who also lost a son, wrote the foreword.

One year after the tragedy, Marilyn's daughter Kelly decided to research gravity flow wagons and to speak about Keith in the Future Farmers of America (FFA) speech contest at Earlham High School. She implored her mother to help, and it was Kelly's request that began moving Marilyn beyond her grief. Darrell constructed a small Plexiglas model of the wagon, loaded it with

popcorn kernels, rested a small plastic figure on top, opened the trap door at the bottom and demonstrated how suction pulled the figure under. Meanwhile, Marilyn contacted Dr. Bill Field at Purdue University who had published a research paper on gravity flow wagons, grain bins and trucks. She became as knowledgeable as possible about the safety features, wishing she had known the dangers when Keith stayed home from school that October day to help his father. Marilyn began turning her grief and knowledge into devotion for prevention and became a public health advocate by helping Kelly research her speech and by starting Farm Safety 4 Just Kids.

Kelly's speech was so well received that she went on to the state contest and won second place. Publicity surrounding her speech and the launching of Farm Safety 4 Just Kids gained wide notice for the issue of farm safety for

Cawshus the Crow, Watchit Scarecrow (Glenna Finney), and Marilyn Adams of Farm Safety 4 Just Kids.

children. The story of a family reaching out for help while trying to cope struck sympathetic cords throughout Iowa and beyond. The media played a crucial role. In 1987, *Wallace's Farmer Magazine, Iowa Farmer Today* and *The New York Times* ran features on Marilyn's personal story and the newly formed organization. *The Wall Street Journal* interviewed Marilyn after a farm safety conference at the University of Iowa dedicated to Keith. *The Boston Globe* printed a series on farm safety. Later Lifetime cable network produced a follow-up story. Marilyn Adams' life now has a special purpose as she surrounds herself with the right people to help prevent injuries and deaths on the farm.

FS4JK's first product – an awareness intervention in the form of a danger decal – became a hit. It read: "Never play in or on the grain. Flowing grain traps and suffocates victim in seconds." The decals were distributed at local farming co-operatives while wagons waited to unload grain. The Iowa FFA state office immediately became interested in assisting with the decal project and helped seek funding to print them.

Marilyn takes delight in recounting the ways Farm Safety 4 Just Kids grew into the successful international organization it is today. Funding from the University of Iowa helped open the FS4JK office in Earlham, followed by funding from Dow Chemical Company. Five years later, funding from Farmland Insurance and Nationwide Insurance Enterprise Company helped start local chapters, and their funding continues to this day. FS4JK has broadened sponsorship to include Cargill, Pioneer Hi-Bred International, Deere & Company and many more corporations involved with agriculture and farms. Marilyn recruits distinguished researchers on farm safety, including Dr. Burton Kross, formerly a University of Iowa expert on groundwater and

her original Chair, to serve as voluntary members of FS4JK's board of directors. A staff of eight in the Earlham offices includes an executive director and directors of operations, chapter relations, community relations and education. Marilyn works closely with Iowa's U.S. senators, Charles Grassley and Tom Harkin, and in the early days she also worked closely with Cooper Evans, agricultural advisor to President George H.W. Bush. Several months after founding the organization, Marilyn testified before a congressional subcommittee. The first lady, Barbara Bush, became an honorary chairperson of the growing organization, visiting two farm safety and health events and lending her expertise on literacy.

Today, FS4JK holds annual training workshops for chapter volunteers. Marilyn and her growing staff developed a three-ring binder field manual called The Chapter Handbook. At the workshops, volunteers share what has worked, what might work, and explore ideas of what a chapter might do. Chapter training now takes place every other year in Des Moines, with well over 100 volunteers attending, and in off years at regional workshops in six to eight states, with as many as 60 volunteers attending each workshop. The training reinforces how to implement programs, how to work with the media and how to raise funds.

Injuries caused by tractor mishaps – rollovers, runovers and entanglements – are still the leading cause of farm fatalities, usually as the result of an extra rider or a young operator. FS4JK develops curricular materials based on the most common injuries. In addition to tractors, the materials cover all-terrain vehicles (ATVs), rural roadways, propane tanks, animal safety, and much more. Training materials include age-appropriate workbooks for school children, teacher manuals, bulletin board ideas, videotapes

Marilyn demonstrates the dangers of a full grain wagon, the kind that took the life of her son, Keith.

Time out to enjoy the family farm.

In 1997 Marilyn wrote "Rhythm of the Seasons: A Journey Beyond Loss," and now travels across the country sharing her story.

Using interactive methods, like this puppet show, Farm Safety 4 Just Kids works to keep rural children safe and healthy.

and giveaways. "Cawshus the Crow," a recurring character in FS4JK brochures, plays a leading role in encouraging children to think about safety. One of FS4JK's most popular (and needed) brochures, "Buckle Up or Eat Glass," reminds teenagers to wear seatbelts and drive safely on rural roads.

FS4JK's prevention and education work has paid dividends. Farm fatalities for children have decreased from over 300 a year at the time Keith died to 104 a year, but nonfatal traumas have increased 10 percent during the same period. In addition to its focus on tractor and ATV safety and other farmstead safety issues, FS4JK is expanding its educational materials to cover rural health issues – groundwater, chemicals, ear and eye protection, food safety and pond safety.

Marilyn's advises those seeking careers in public health to find a position that makes a difference in a child's life. She sees careers in public health as rewarding because they have the potential to positively impact the lives of children.

As for the future, Marilyn foresees many changes. She cautions that mind-set needs to be open to change if emerging risks are to be handled for all generations. In her position as a member of the External Board of Advisors of the College of Public Health at the University of Iowa, she enjoys knowing there is a fair and frank exchange of ideas between students and professors. She values the collaboration of professors and staff members of the College of Public Health in helping the External Board of Advisors recommend curricular and policy directions. Marilyn brings to the table her experience living on family farms her whole life and her tragic firsthand knowledge of the health and safety risks for children.

Marilyn Adams found the strength to turn a devastating personal loss into a gain for farm families. She loves the 800-acre farm where she and Darrell live and grow corn and soybeans, and she has no thoughts of retiring or living elsewhere. Her own mother, now in her early 80s, just retired from a long working career at a state hospital. She and Darrell and their 11 grandchildren paddle boat and fish on the seven-acre farm pond for catfish, large mouth bass and blue gills. The rolling fields invite her to contemplate Keith's too-short life, secure in knowing the staff of Farm Safety 4 Just Kids three miles away in Earlham is busy making a difference so that others don't suffer the profound grief she felt after losing a child. Marilyn herself travels near and far to spread the word about farm safety and health for children. Having found her life's work making the family farm a healthy workplace, she gives others hope that farm injuries will decrease dramatically and deaths of children on farms will be made even more rare.

A. Cornelius Baker

District of Columbia

*Providing access to HIV/AIDS treatment
for people in need*

Every month Unity of Washington, a small church congregation, sends a check to Whitman-Walker Clinic in Washington, D.C., to help in the fight against AIDS. Sometimes it is a few hundred dollars, sometimes $2,000 or more. Over the years, these donations have totaled nearly $65,000. Unity of Washington is just one example of how communities of faith assist community-based organizations in the fight against AIDS. Across the metropolitan region surrounding Washington, D.C., groups of virtually every faith put their beliefs into action by making generous contributions of volunteer time and money to Whitman-Walker Clinic. These efforts not only fund the clinic's programs, they remind each congregation that HIV/AIDS impacts family, friends, neighbors and fellow congregants.

Spearheading the critical fund-raising function for Whitman-Walker Clinic is A. Cornelius Baker. He joined the clinic as executive director in 1999 after a varied career as an arts critic, political activist, government worker and policy director of a national AIDS organization. As Whitman-Walker Clinic depends on generous gifts from corporate sponsors, small businesses, foundations and individual donors, Cornelius' diverse background enables him to move with confidence among these many audiences. The donations allow the clinic to provide health services to thousands of gay, lesbian, bisexual and transgender people throughout the greater Washington metropolitan area with a special focus on HIV/AIDS.

A. Cornelius Baker was born in Sodus Point on Lake Ontario in upstate New York, but grew up in Syracuse. He attended Corcoran High School, where he was active in theater and graduated early in January 1979. He immediately enrolled at Eisenhower College in Seneca Falls, New York, as a freshman. At Eisenhower College (now absorbed into the Rochester Institute of Technology), Cornelius majored in comparative literature and took the required four-year core curriculum, World Studies, which focused on the classics, humanities and sciences and provided him broad-based learning that was deep and rich. During his junior and senior years he directed theater productions, leading him to consider arts administration, specifically artistic programming, as a career. In his last semester ending in May 1983, he participated in the Washington Semester at American University and interned at the Kennedy Center in the Alliance for Arts Education. That experience cemented his calling of bringing the arts to people.

After graduating from Eisenhower College, Cornelius settled in Washington, D.C., where he has been an active member of the gay community

ever since. In his first job as a writer on the arts with *City Paper*, he reviewed theater productions and cinema in a column called "City Lights." In May 1984, spurred toward politics by his excitement over Jesse Jackson's presidential campaign, Cornelius left *City Paper* to join the staff of Carol Schwartz, a Republican contending for a city council nomination in a primary election. Her opponent was a black conservative Baptist minister, and although the black community was largely Democratic, it supported him in the Republican primary.

Cornelius gravitated to Carol Schwartz because he admired her openness and progressive politics, and because he felt she was being unfairly attacked. A native of Midland, Texas, Carol raised her three children in the District and sent them to public schools. She became a community activist and served on the School Board. Cornelius became a key organizer for her in the restive gay community. The Stonewall incident in New York City in 1969 had energized gay political activism, which by 1984 had found full voice with the AIDS epidemic, a catastrophe recognized only in the preceding two years. In a surprising result, Carol Schwartz won the primary and went on to win the City Council seat in the general election. Cornelius joined her staff part time, working also at the "Friends of the Kennedy Center" for a year until a full-time position opened on her staff. Cornelius served Carol for four years until the end of her term; she chose not to run again for City Council after her husband's suicide in 1989.

In late 1988, Cornelius began work for the George H.W. Bush Presidential Inaugural Committee. There, he met Ron Kaufman, later to become deputy assistant to the president for personnel, who became a mentor. In 1989, with Ron's assistance, Cornelius was made a presiden-

tial appointee at the Department of Health and Human Services under Secretary Louis Sullivan. Cornelius became a confidential assistant to an assistant secretary for health, Jim Mason. Jim Mason later assigned Cornelius to the HIV/AIDS office, where he acted as a liaison to national AIDS organizations and worked with regional health officers and others in low prevalence but newly emerging areas such as Nebraska and Wyoming.

In 1992, Cornelius became the first policy director of the National Association of People with AIDS (NAPWA), a nonprofit organization. He was a policy division of one and had to determine how to build the policy role of the organization in a challenging funding environment. His staff grew to four people in an overall staff of 13 people, and he successfully won over a donor community skeptical of his service in the Bush administration. In 1995, he also advocated in Congress for continued funding for the AIDS Education and Training Centers, part of the Ryan White CARE Act. After the 1994 midterm election, Congress threatened to kill funding for the centers. Only the Herculean efforts of Cornelius and others to educate members of Congress on their benefits saved the centers, which proved fortunate. Several years later, with new treatments available for HIV/AIDS, the centers became the front-line in training physicians how to use the new treatments. As testament to his success at NAPWA, the Paul Rappaport Foundation became an especially generous donor and in 1996 Cornelius became the executive director.

Three years later, in 1999, Cornelius joined the Whitman-Walker Clinic as executive director. When he joined the clinic, Cornelius had been active in fighting the AIDS epidemic since the mid-1980s. His success in the clinic position, a perfect fit for him, evolved from his political

activism, love of Washington, D.C., and commitment to gay and lesbian issues. His career path had taken him a long way from his original dream of a career in arts programming.

Whitman-Walker Clinic, founded as a gay men's STD clinic, is named after Walt Whitman, the American poet who served as a nurse during the Civil War after his brother was wounded in the Battle of Fredericksburg, and Mary Walker, one of the first women physicians in the United States. Because she wore bloomers, Congress rescinded Dr. Walker's Medal of Honor, awarded for service during the Civil War; it was not until 100 years later that President Jimmy Carter reinstated the medal. Originally part of the Washington Free Clinic, Whitman-Walker Clinic split off in 1978 to become its own program with a primary focus on gay and lesbian health issues. Whitman-Walker Clinic is especially committed to ending the suffering of all those infected and affected by HIV/AIDS. Of the six incorporators, half are still alive, with Dr. John Stansel (now at San Francisco General Hospital) perhaps the best-known.

In 2003, the clinic served 14,000 people — 7,000 for HIV testing and 7,000 for ongoing clinical services — a productive community-based health center contracted with the D.C. Department of Health and with health departments in Montgomery and Prince Georges Counties in Maryland and Alexandria City, Arlington County and Fairfax County in Virginia. Among the services offered beyond medical services are a laboratory, dental services, behavioral counseling, case management, addiction services, a housing program, a food bank, legal services, and ongoing health prevention education. In addition to prosecuting anti-discrimination cases, the legal services group promotes family reunification for immigrants.

Whitman-Walker Clinic administers four sites: two in D.C. in DuPont Circle and Anacostia, one in Arlington, Virginia, and one in Tacoma Park, Maryland. The staff numbered 260 when Cornelius became executive director in 1999; five years later it stood at 275, including 54 medical staff. The Ryan White CARE Act, a federal program, is a primary source of funding for the clinic. Prevention grants from the Centers for Disease Control and Prevention in Atlanta and joint programming with the National Institutes of Health in Bethesda — desk-bound physicians keep their clinical skills sharp by rotating through — also help the clinic provide services. From 2001 to 2003, however, the clinic fell $3 million short in anticipated revenues due to the tough fund-raising environment during those years.

Funding has always been the biggest challenge for Whitman-Walker Clinic. In the face of a projected $250,000 deficit in D.C. in 2004, the clinic eliminated 20 positions early in the year but kept intact its capacity for client services. Such budget quandaries force Cornelius to make choices, limiting either the number of clients served or the level of services provided. As executive director, Cornelius decides how to ration care only after consulting closely with his board of directors and key staff members. In the current climate of nursing shortages, exacerbated by the competitive health care environment in greater Washington, he knows he will face rising costs for nursing salaries for the foreseeable future. In order to remain a state-of-the-art facility, he must keep pace with advances in medical technology and replace computers every three years. Achieving these goals becomes much more challenging in the face of funding shortfalls.

The Whitman-Walker Clinic relies on public funds from the federal, state and local levels, which together account for 52 percent of annual

Working with children.

In the office with colleague
Philippe Chiliade.

revenues. Third-party payments account for 3 percent of revenues, and private fund-raising accounts for the remaining 44 percent. The Meyer Foundation and the Community Foundation, both based in Washington, D.C., have been among the most generous private foundations. The foundations at Fannie Mae and Freddie Mac also have been generous sources of funds, and Pepco a generous corporate supporter. Often small family foundations approach the clinic unsolicited, asking how they can help. Additional revenues come from an annual gala and the National AIDS Marathon Training Program. The training program, a major commitment of time and effort for 2,160 participants, raised $2.9 million in 2003 for vital medical and social services for clinic clients. Despite having lived with HIV for 20 years, Cornelius has run in the Marine Corps Marathon in Washington and the Mardi Gras Marathon in New Orleans to raise much-needed funds for Whitman-Walker Clinic.

As part of his duties as executive director, Cornelius considers new ways to cultivate revenue streams. Possible new sources are a thrift store and training-based retail sales. Faced with the need to be vigilant about expenses, he constantly weighs costs and benefits. He finds that the current federal budget climate, with ballooning deficits, pressures Whitman-Walker Clinic to ration care. Because more than nine out of 10 clients have annual incomes of $12,000 or less, with nowhere else to turn for medical treatment, social and legal services, food and housing, Cornelius and his board of directors have pledged that those most in need must rely on Whitman-Walker Clinic. Their goal is to be an effective, trusted source of health services and education, not just a well-funded agency. Incidentally, the Honorable Carol Schwartz, once again a member of the City Council, is a director.

Cornelius advises people considering careers in public health that the greatest good they can do is to play a bedrock role in building a healthy community. In his case, with no direct public health training, he learned by listening. He advises everyone to listen carefully to community needs, to the people served, to leaders and to their own motivations.

Looking towards the future, Cornelius sees the nation at an interesting juncture, one that should allow public health to show its merit, prove its value and serve the nation well. The challenge for public health continues to be to interrupt the flow of communicable diseases, while mustering resources to confront emerging diseases such as HIV and SARS. A wholly new challenge is to build systems to combat potential acts of bioterrorism.

Cornelius would like to see greater investment in community-based health care systems, with a focus on access and prevention. He views vaccines and effective sex education (not just abstinence) as fundamental to achieving prevention. The challenges he foresees at the Whitman-Walker Clinic, besides funding, are to build cultural competency in the staff, encourage participation by minorities in public health careers, and make primary care more accessible. Increasingly, the clinic serves Spanish-speaking clients and immigrants from Africa. Cornelius worries that the clinic staff has yet to fully master the culturally sensitive approaches these diverse clients require, although fully 20 percent of the staff speaks Spanish. Cornelius also worries that the public health infrastructure has yet to ensure that every person gets to see a doctor.

A. Cornelius Baker is currently a member of the U.S. Department of Health and Human Services Panel on Clinical Practices in HIV Treatment, the U.S. Public Health Service/Infectious Disease

Society of America's Working Group on the Prevention of Opportunistic Infections, and the Centers for Disease Control and Prevention Advisory Committee on HIV/AIDS. Until recently, he served as founding co-chair of the National Coalition for LGBT Health. Through his national contributions, Cornelius enhances Whitman-Walker Clinic's prominence among community-based health centers.

Each day at the Whitman-Walker Clinic, the staff and volunteers participate in a mission of life. They provide medical care or social services to someone living with HIV, counsel a gay, lesbian, bisexual or transgender person, or provide administrative support to a myriad of programs. Each day, they know their actions help save and enhance the lives of every client they touch. Amidst his hard and necessary work to guarantee the future of the clinic, Executive Director A. Cornelius Baker takes heart from good deeds performed each and every day.

Jane Conard, RN

Alaska

Bringing access to health care to remote communities

Bethel, a bush town on the Kuskokwim River, lies 400 miles due west of Anchorage in southwest Alaska. Surrounded by tundra – a flat, treeless, windswept landscape with thousands of ponds and small lakes, the result of seasonal warming of the permafrost – Bethel has only five miles of paved roads and a population under 7,000. In the winter when the Kuskokwim freezes over, inhabitants drive at low speed on the river (avoiding braking with all their wheels in chains) to nearby villages. Otherwise, the only way out of Bethel is by boat in the summer and plane throughout the year. Even though Alaskans are inveterate travelers, a round-trip airfare from Bethel to Anchorage that costs more than $400 keeps inhabitants close to home in seeking distractions. Many hunt and fish, but the tundra is otherwise inhospitable to most activities.

The presence of bears reminds the people of Bethel that they are not at the top of the food chain. Someone can disappear in no time in an area so unpopulated, leading to fear of isolation and motivating people to be active in the community. A common choice of native families in the area is subsistence, with the husband hunting for game (such as moose) and fishing to harvest enough protein for the entire extended family for a year. Family members pitch in as best they can to ensure survival, both financial and nutritional. In the traditional villages, men work in construction or as mechanics, if they are fortunate enough to be employed. Women observe traditional gender roles by working as clerks and teachers or in childcare or health care.

Into this forbidding landscape, Jane Conard arrived from Missouri on Friday, October 13, 1989, to work as an itinerant nurse serving the native Yup'ik people. Her work took her to 39 villages in a 45,000 square mile district with a population, mostly Eskimo, of 23,000. Jane had just completed her bachelor's degree in nursing at Webster University in St. Louis. Like many other new arrivals in Alaska, she had been recruited from the lower 48. Alaska appealed to her in part because her husband's uncle had worked on the Trans-Alaska Pipeline Project and encouraged her to give it a try. Jane left for Alaska on her own to see if she could make a go of it. Her family followed 10 months later.

Jane's husband Ray landed a job as the audiovisual coordinator at the Kuskokwim branch of the University of Alaska-Fairbanks system, but died 18 months later from heart disease. Diagnosed only after he arrived in Bethel, he sought treatment in Portland, Oregon, and struggled through a long period of decline. Jane's three children – 10, 12 and 15 years old when they arrived in Bethel – entered local schools and never looked back. After her husband died, Jane sent the children to stay with relatives in Missouri for the summer, letting them know they could remain there. When Jane flew to Missouri at the end of the summer, thinking she might be leaving Alaska behind for good, her eldest daughter, never in love with Bethel, asserted that Alaska was now home and insisted on returning. She found that her friends in Missouri were frustratingly narrow in their worldview – for example, their lives revolved around cars, whereas in Bethel with five miles of paved roads, that decidedly was not the case.

Jane was born in Davis Crossing, Missouri, in the foothills of the Ozarks in southeast Missouri. She grew up on a small farm, the eldest of four siblings, while her father worked in a nearby lead mine and later in an iron mine, both developed by the French in 1720. The mines had been fortified during the Civil War but both closed for good in the 1960s. She attended Mitchell Elementary School, then Leadwood (now West County) High School. Teachers in the largely rural high school emphasized the importance of a college education. At home, she received the same encouragement – her mother, originally from Richmond in northwest Missouri, attended Central Missouri State University in Warrensburg.

Jane chose to attend Mineral Area Junior College in Flat River on a yearbook scholarship, staying close to home rather than heading to the University of Missouri in Columbia for journalism, a choice she also considered. She loved science and wanted to be a geneticist. She points out that farm daughters in general are driven to get things done, and done right, and are used to authority and directing things. She completed an associate's degree in the liberal arts, and after a year of work as an attendant at Farmington State Hospital, a psychiatric hospital, she returned to Mineral Area Junior College to earn an associate degree in nursing. In 1974, during the year she worked, Jane married Ray, an electronics technician, and gave up her idea of attending Southern Illinois University in Carbondale. Working at the hospital, she discovered that her efforts improved people's lives considerably.

During the years of raising her children in Missouri, Jane participated in their full lives while working full time as an intensive care nurse at a hospital in Farmington and later as a public health nurse at the St. Francis County

Health Center in Park Hills. In 1987 she began attending Webster University in St. Louis to earn her bachelor's degree in nursing. For two years, three evenings a week, she shared driving duties with two fellow students, commuting an hour and a half each way for classes.

When she arrived in Bethel, Jane was one of eight itinerant nurses serving the region. Over the years, this staff grew to 13 in addition to the Bethel Health Center staff. Ten itinerant nurses serve the region now. Jane has served as nurse manager for five years, a position she also held twice in the 1990s in two-year and three-year stints. The state government position reports to a regional nurse manager (currently vacant) who reports to a section chief in the Section of Nursing in the Division of Public Health. This division is part of the Department of Health and Social Services in Juneau, the state capital.

Alaska's population of 600,000 is spread across 585,000 square miles, making it the least populated state in the United States. This huge area is divided into very few seats of government. The state government in Juneau controls large swaths of land throughout the state, including the Bethel district. Half of Alaska's population lives in and around Anchorage, which is run by a municipal government. Another third lives in and around Fairbanks, which is split between a municipal and borough government. Unique to Alaska are the native corporations, created by a compact between nine tribes of Native Alaskans and the federal government during the Carter administration to compensate the tribes for ceding large areas of their lands as national parks and forests. The compact brought tribe members several billion dollars that they manage through the corporations, in both service-oriented and profit-making activities.

Over the years, Jane has had to refocus her staff on population-based health care and systems rather than on individualized care. In her supervisory role, she works with the itinerant nurses to improve skills. She consistently asks them, "For you to feel good about your job, what do I need to do?" In the villages, itinerant nurses ask patients, "What are your top three health concerns?" By seeing through others' eyes, validating and empowering another culture, nurses help solve problems within the culture. They help people discover ownership of the problem and its solution.

Jane and her staff, almost all from the lower 48, revel in getting to know the local customs. The Yup'iks learn kinetically and learn best by being shown, not told, how to do something. They speak in quiet voices – the native language is full of low guttural sounds – and believe that making eye contact and asking questions are rude, complicating the nursing process. Consensus drives decision-making and the people do not allow one person to speak for them. A key concern is mental health – suicides are 13 percent above the national average – that includes such issues as loss of identity and substance abuse. In the late 1940s and 1950s, the Yukon-Kuskokwim Delta had the highest incidence of tuberculosis in the world. Today, alcoholism is endemic.

Jane finds the nurses she supervises to be largely autonomous and likens her job (with a smile) to harnessing a bunch of cats running in the Iditarod. The itinerant nurses, by definition, must be independent to do the job. They are all based in Bethel, allowing for staff meetings and shared insights on how to network, mobilize partnerships and secure resources. The state government recently went through a contentious reorganization that affected public health nursing.

Cold-water kayaking in
Whittier with her
daughter Davonna.

With colleague
Bernice Ivers, AC3.

On a trip up the Kuskokwim River
to McGrath with Ross Boring.

Jane in her Anchorage office.

Jane focuses on transitioning services that can be profit-making to the native corporation in Bethel, which runs the hospital, and to other providers. The corporation has superseded the Indian Health Service, once pervasive throughout Alaska. Bethel's 52-bed hospital, the largest in the Alaskan bush, also provides dental, optometry and many other services. Much of Bethel's population is transient, spending two years under contract for specific services and then moving on.

Jane's itinerant nurses take regular flights to the villages, accompanying the mail, aboard so-called "bush taxis" – seven-seat 207 Cessnas. They pack medical equipment, vaccines, sleeping bags, water, food and clothes for a week, usually in eight to 10 large bags that weigh up to a total of 180 pounds. In the villages, nurses live in clinics and provide services that include prenatal visits, immunizations, well-child screenings, communicable disease services, TB screening and management as well as community presentations. This "western" model of medicine has replaced the village Shamans of the 19th century. The itinerant nurses collaborate with Community Health Aides who live and provide care in their villages year-round. The nurses depend on these skilled paraprofessionals for translation and expertise about the village.

Alaska is a place where people can reinvent themselves. Jane Conard kept being herself, and through the years became a distinguished citizen of Bethel. In the community, volunteers get many things done, and Jane contributes her time and skills to improve the lives of others. She learned many new skills along the way – fixing heaters, water pumps and toilets are almost second nature to her now. Although electricity is usually reliable, every citizen of Bethel stocks backups – piles of wood to light wood-burning stoves and a cache

of bottled water and food – in case the worst happens. Jane also took one year to study women's health in California, earning a certificate as a nurse practitioner in women's health.

As Jane Conard contemplates the future, she sees herself relocating to Anchorage after retirement, to save her children the $400+ it takes to fly round-trip to Bethel. She already owns a condominium in Anchorage where her youngest child, a daughter, lives while studying at the University of Alaska-Anchorage. Her eldest daughter currently works in Vanuatu, an island nation in the South Pacific, as a Peace Corps volunteer helping the provincial government develop "cottage industry." Her son and his wife have settled in Palm Desert, California, where he enrolled in college after serving in the Army for four years in Korea, Kuwait and throughout the war in Iraq. E-mail messages keep the family very much in touch. Other than travel and, after retirement, a possible stint in the Peace Corps with her youngest daughter, Jane has no intention of leaving Alaska. The years in Bethel and in the bush have made their mark and she has, despite herself, been reinvented.

Debbie McCune Davis

Arizona

Protecting children's health through immunization

While many health professionals have crossed over into politics as a result of their community involvement, the reverse path is less common. One such person, Debbie McCune Davis, transformed her long political service into a public health mission. Debbie has been the program director of The Arizona Partnership for Immunization (TAPI) since 1996. After serving in the Arizona House of Representatives from 1979 through 1994, she was fortunate to develop a career in the private sector in the field she cared for most – maternal and child health. Through TAPI, Debbie brings together public and private health organizations and providers in Arizona, entities that had little contact with one another previously, to collaborate and achieve the state's immunization goals. As the most influential advocate for immunizations in Arizona, she has made TAPI a model program for the nation.

To date, more than 400 public/private individuals and groups participate on TAPI committees and projects. Participants include physicians, health plans, Arizona's Medicaid organization AHCCCS (Arizona Health Care Cost Containment System), vaccine manufacturers, county health departments, community health centers, the state health department, and many other advocates for immunization throughout the state. Having accomplished all this without formal public health training, Debbie demonstrates the passion that public health people get to feel and is a unique face in the field.

Born Debbie Ponte in the small town of Port Vue near McKeesport in western Pennsylvania, Debbie moved with her parents and two younger sisters to Phoenix when she was 13 years old. Her father was an auto mechanic who had been hit once too often by falling ice when he crawled under cars to fix them. A warmer climate proved hard to resist.

Debbie attended Washington High School in Phoenix. She became involved in student government when she was elected to the student council during her junior year and remained very involved with her youth group at church. After graduating in 1969, she enrolled at Glendale Community College, intending to major in home economics. She took an introductory sociology course in her first semester, however, and grew fascinated with how good public policy makes a difference in people's lives. After graduating in 1971 with an associate degree, Debbie enrolled at Arizona State University (ASU) in Tempe and majored in sociology.

Debbie had married William McCune during her second year at Glendale Community College and after a semester at ASU she took time off to have two children, Cara and Michael, born in 1972 and 1973. Meanwhile, her husband had been elected to the Arizona House of Representatives in 1970 and would be elected to the State Senate in 1974. As both a young mother and the wife of a politician, Debbie became involved in the community. Acting as an additional pair of eyes and ears for her husband, she contributed to his success as an elected representative. After resuming her course work at ASU, Debbie graduated midyear in 1975 and began working part time selling life insurance while she explored ways to put her sociology background to use through community relations work.

In 1978, a state representative seat opened up in Debbie's district. She ran for the seat as a Democrat and at 27 years of age became the youngest woman ever elected to the Arizona House of Representatives up to that time. Her first committees were Human Resources and Banking & Insurance, but over the course of her career in elected office she served on nearly every committee except Health, Education and Ways & Means.

In 1980, 10 days after she was re-elected, Debbie gave birth to her third child and second daughter, Courtney. Her own experience with childbirth led her to focus on maternal and child health issues, and she became a leading advocate for changes in Arizona. In particular, she focused on babies in rural communities who were not surviving due to inadequate perinatal care. She worked with her fellow legislators and helped develop a plan to transport women from rural communities to urban hospitals to deliver their babies. Urban hospital centers were far better equipped to handle any perinatal crises that arose during childbirth, and when the State Legislature enacted a new delivery system for obstetrics, infant survival improved.

In 1987, Debbie and her husband divorced and she began work with a local behavioral health agency in Maricopa County, dealing with drug and alcohol abuse, methadone maintenance and with the chronically mentally ill. She learned about community needs, about trust relationships and about cultural diversity issues. She also learned that clients needed to be treated holistically. A domestic violence shelter, for example, might be treating someone who also had a drug addiction. Debbie turned what she learned into proposals to improve mental health services in Arizona and rallied her fellow legislators into backing them.

On January 1, 1990, Debbie remarried. Her new husband, Glenn Davis, is an attorney who from 1980 to 1984 also served in the State Legislature. Glenn and his former wife had adopted Joshua, a special needs child who Debbie also helped raise. Later in 1990, Debbie and Glenn had a daughter, Lauren. Debbie was deemed a high-risk pregnancy when preterm labor set in at five months and she spent the last months of the pregnancy in bed. Her daughter, now in junior high school, is doing very well. Little did Debbie know at the time that she would become one of the most influential people in Arizona in the field of maternal and child health.

In 1994, Debbie left the State Legislature to run for the Corporation Commission, a statewide office. After losing the election, she faced decisions about what she wanted to do next. She knew her strengths – fund-raising, community coordinating – but had to discover where they best fit in the private sector. It was not until February 1996 that she joined The Arizona Partnership for Immunization. Even then, she had to be talked into taking the job. Once on board, however, she was and continues to be a dynamo. The standards set by TAPI make it a model organization and Arizona a leading state in the nation for childhood immunization partnerships.

At TAPI, Debbie strives to meet the Healthy People 2010 goal of achieving 90 percent vaccine coverage by children's second birthdays, enough coverage to create herd immunity and protect those who are not properly vaccinated. Rather than delivering services directly, the Arizona Department of Health Services contracts with TAPI to build and maintain a collaborative network of community partners who in turn deliver the immunization services. In 1991, the two-year-old vaccination rate in Arizona was 46 percent.

In 2004, it is 79 percent. Debbie foresees immunization rates reaching 90 percent in two to three years if funding remains stable and the delivery systems hold up. Currently, 13 vaccines are required or recommended before a child turns 2 – MMR (measles mumps rubella), Hib, polio, DPT and hepatitis B are required, and hepatitis A, pneumonia, chicken pox, influenza and a DPT booster are recommended. The 13 vaccines (some shots are multivalent) cost $600 on average. TAPI works to ensure that vaccines are available for low-income uninsured children and lobbies the State Legislature to make vaccines available for the underinsured as well.

Many successes have resulted from TAPI's collaboration with partners. Paramedics with the Phoenix Fire Department administer shots in Spanish-speaking neighborhoods. From 1998 to 2001, well-child visits increased 20 percent for the Medicaid population. Community health centers improved flu vaccine coverage by identifying children at high risk with such diseases as asthma and diabetes.

Debbie believes TAPI's most significant accomplishment is the funding secured from the Flinn Foundation to help build a central immunization database. Called the Arizona State Immunization Information System (ASIIS), this registry is housed at the Arizona Department of Health Services and is updated continually to allow providers to look up information on immunizations given elsewhere in the state, and often elsewhere in the country. TAPI lobbied the State Legislature in 1996 to enact the registry and rallied the physician community to back it and secure the most comprehensive plan possible. Launched in January 1998, ASIIS has become a tool used in physician's offices and clinics to improve the immunization status of children.

Outside the Arizona state capitol with colleagues (l to r) Tara Plese, Martin Quezada, John Dynesman.

At her daughter Lauren's softball game with husband Glenn.

With lobbyists in front of the Arizona House of Representatives, from left, Ed Wren, Tara Plese, Martin Quezada, and Helena Whitney.

Reviewing a successful event with members of The Arizona Partnership for Immunization, (l to r) Jim McPherson, Jennifer Tinney, and Dr. Dan Aspery.

With the registry now regarded as a given among Arizona's health care community, the number of users of the database continues to grow. The benefits are many. For example, school nurses find it useful to check on the immunization history of students newly arrived in their school. Meanwhile, referrals for unnecessary vaccines have been greatly reduced, saving money and keeping children in school. Maricopa County, the state's largest, has determined the registry saves them $13,000 a month in avoiding second dosing. The registry also allows Child Protective Services to place children quickly, a real advantage in what is often a crisis situation. The registry has also driven managed care partners to improve immunization rates and allows WIC to screen records and refer children to clinics for vaccinations, aware that uninsured parents might overlook them. Furthermore, when a devastating fire burned 500,000 acres and displaced 25,000 residents in one rural county, the registry restored the immunization records immediately.

Debbie's work at TAPI is greatly assisted by a dedicated board of directors, 20 members at any given time who volunteer their services. Dr. Daniel Cloud, a retired pediatric surgeon, serves as the chair of the Steering Committee. He lends stature to the project and encourages creative strategies for improving the rates of childhood immunizations in Arizona. While Arizona once lagged in national rankings, it is now above the median among the 50 states. TAPI has won national recognition for its success in collaborating with a wide range of partners in advancing childhood immunizations in Arizona.

Debbie feels that public health is perhaps the most satisfying career one can work in. She believes that living in a healthy community, where the burdens of chronic disease and the fear of infectious disease have been made manageable,

has enormous value. Debbie foresees that public health 10 years from now will be defined more as community health. She believes the focus will be on preventing chronic conditions through a heightened awareness of smoking, air and water quality and food, and that individual responsibility will grow.

In 2002, fearing that funding cutbacks threatened the programs she cared most about, Debbie ran again for the Arizona House of Representatives and won. As a legislator once again in the part-time State Legislature, she has cut back on the time she spends at TAPI but continues with her key responsibilities of managing the project, fund-raising and grant writing. She finds that the skills she honed in her political career – fund-raising, consensus building, listening to and working with people from diverse backgrounds – come into play every day in her work for TAPI. Fortunately, the funding community readily supports TAPI because it is outcome driven.

In the current environment of state budget cuts, Debbie has been able to defend the central database and educate her fellow legislators about the benefits of immunization services and the cost savings the registry has produced. TAPI publishes a quarterly newsletter, *Upshots*, mailed to thousands of immunization partners and interested individuals throughout the state. Debbie is a driving force behind TAPI activities, events, boards and committees and has expanded the original mission to include immunization advocacy and education from birth through adulthood. She plays an active role on the national stage as well, serving as a founding member of AIRA (American Immunization Registry Association) and as a board member of NPI (National Partnership for Immunization). She serves on working committees of the "Every Child by Two" organi-

zation based in Washington, D. C., developing training materials and improving the working relationship between immunization registries and managed care organizations. She also serves on the planning committees for the NCIC (National Conference on Immunization Coalitions) and served as host of the Fifth National Conference, held in Phoenix in 2003.

Debbie McCune Davis finds that sharing what works well in other states helps energize partners in The Arizona Partnership for Immunization to try new strategies to improve outcomes in her home state. She continues to bring new partners into the coalition, creating new synergies. As both a legislator and a public health professional, Debbie makes a tangible difference for the people of Arizona.

Kathleen Falk, JD

Wisconsin

Controlling urban development to ensure the community's environmental health

Suburban sprawl can be a threat to the public's health in many ways, both visible and invisible. Traffic congestion breeds air pollution and stress. Dense development reduces options for physical exercise. Habitat loss diminishes the reassurance that most people find in the natural order of rolling meadow, streams and woodlands. In Dane County, Wisconsin – the home of the state capital, Madison – citizens have participated in a variety of approaches to control sprawl. Under the leadership of County Executive Kathleen Falk, local government and citizens came together in 1998 to support an important first step in land-use planning. The initiative, called "Design Dane," promoted sensible growth. Another initiative, called "Farms and Neighborhoods: Making Both Strong," quickly followed. In 1999, a Conservation Fund referendum that passed with more than 75 percent of the vote called for conserving open space by protecting large tracts of parkland and natural areas from development. In 2004, Dane County citizens came together again under Kathleen's leadership to support a new initiative

called "Attain Dane!" This new initiative brings together citizens, businesses, associations and local government units to create "build out plans" that identify the best long-term development patterns.

Kathleen's contributions to the environmental health of her county demonstrate her belief that all citizens should play a role in protecting the public's health and in serving the public interest. Although not trained as a public health professional, Kathleen works to mobilize Dane County citizens to focus on a healthier environment. A healthy environment promotes sustainable development that is ecologically sound. It also provides an improving standard of living, access to safe food and water, and the means for physical and mental development. A healthy environment encourages full and equal citizen participation in land use planning and decision-making.

Kathleen was born in Milwaukee, the eldest of four children in a German-Irish family that valued land and conservation. When Kathleen was seven, the family moved to Waukesha County, 15 miles west of Milwaukee, first to a rural area and then into town. Kathleen graduated from Catholic Memorial High School and began college at the two-year branch of the University of Wisconsin system in Waukesha, transferring for the last semester of her sophomore year to the University of Wisconsin-Madison as a major in mathematics. At Waukesha, she typed manuscripts for professor Hung-Mao Tien, now the Taiwanese ambassador to Great Britain but then a professor of political science and international relations. He recognized her academic promise and encouraged her to transfer to Stanford University on a full scholarship, which she did for her junior and senior years. At Stanford, Kathleen switched majors from mathematics to philosophy when she realized the many logic courses she had taken, which she

loved, fulfilled philosophy requirements. She also found a compatible home for two years at the all-male Newman Center on campus, where she broke the gender barrier and became fast friends with the resident priests.

After graduating from Stanford in 1973, Kathleen returned to Wisconsin to attend the University of Wisconsin-Madison Law School, earning her law degree in 1976. There, she took courses from Jim McDonald, a leading environmental advocate. The federal ban on DDT had recently taken effect, and Kathleen revered Rachel Carson, still very much in the news, as the catalyst of the environmental movement. Kathleen maintained her strong interest in environmental law with her first job. From 1977 to 1983, just out of law school with a starting salary of $35 per week, she served as co-director and general counsel of Wisconsin's Environmental Decade, a statewide nonprofit citizens' environmental protection organization. In this role, she won nationally significant litigation to protect citizens' rights in cases involving public utilities.

From 1983 to 1997, Kathleen served as an assistant attorney general in the Wisconsin Department of Justice. For most of those years, from 1983 to 1995, she also served as Wisconsin's public intervenor, a position that statutorily authorized her to protect the public's rights in natural resources by taking any appropriate legal action. Governor Warren Knowles created the position of public intervenor in 1965 as a watchdog agency to protect the public interest within the state government bureaucracy. Governor Tommy Thompson and the Wisconsin State Legislature eliminated the position in 1995. One reason the public intervenor position worked well was that the Citizens Advisory Board, a rotating group of citizen advisers, lent perspective on which cases to pursue and on what needed to be done.

As public intervenor, Kathleen focused on land-use and transportation issues while her colleague Tom Dawson worked on pesticides and toxins. Kathleen litigated successfully to protect public access to the Summerfest Grounds in downtown Milwaukee, for example, when commercial development along the Lake Michigan shoreline threatened to block it. She also successfully litigated against the State Department of Transportation (DOT), winning a lawsuit intended to increase investment in mass transit. The state budgeted $1 billion every two years for highway construction, and the lawsuit also required the DOT to file environmental impact statements. In the early 1980s, she and Tom Dawson worked together on citizens' "right to know" and public trust issues.

Dane County has a population of 450,000, with 250,000 of that total living in small cities, towns, villages and rural areas outside the city of Madison. The fastest growth in the county's population occurs outside Madison, primarily in a number of burgeoning suburbs along the interstate highway. One of nine counties in the state with a county executive form of government, Dane County first elected Kathleen as its county executive in 1997 in a nonpartisan election. She was re-elected in 2001 and plans to run again in 2005. In 2002, Kathleen ran in the Democratic primary for governor, the first major party woman candidate for governor in Wisconsin history. She lost a hard-fought race to the current governor, Jim Doyle.

The county executive form of government in Wisconsin is a strong one and provides broad veto power to the county executive. The county legislature, called the Board of Supervisors, has 37 members who are elected in nonpartisan elections every two years. Bolstered by her strong governing authority, Kathleen runs a tight ship,

earning Dane County a Triple A bond rating, one of only two in the state. She limits tax increases by making county government more efficient, consolidating agencies and seeking cost-effective innovations. The annual budget is approximately $400 million, of which $200 million goes to Human Services – disabilities, mental health, public health, substance abuse, aging and youth programs, among others. The county's other responsibilities include the airport, the courts, environmental protection, highways, law enforcement, parks and the zoo.

As county executive, Kathleen's two priorities are planning for rapid population growth in areas outside Madison and kids. When done well, land-use planning not only conserves open space and contains sprawl, it also improves a growing population's health by promoting a healthy environment. A healthy environment depends on citizens who take ownership of the issues. To achieve this, Kathleen proposed the "Design Dane" and "Attain Dane!" initiatives, as well as the Conservation Fund referendum, as strategies for involving citizens in shaping a consensus approach to containing sprawl.

Through proposed transfers and purchases of development rights, the county would keep farmland from being developed and would keep natural areas "forever wild." Working with local government units, the county regulates development on the outskirts of small cities and towns that often results in intergovernmental conflicts. To reduce competition for development by these cities and towns – a race for developers' dollars that often results in poor planning – the county would implement a tax base sharing system that spreads fairly the rewards and risks of development among localities. Ideally, there would be no winners or losers. For developers, the "build out" plans would make building sites predictable.

In these designated "build out" areas, the infrastructure of suburban life – housing, commercial and industrial districts, roads, sewers, schools – would be planned carefully in advance to coexist with open spaces and improve the overall quality of life.

Kathleen oversees many activities related to public health in Dane County that go beyond her role of overseeing the Dane County Department of Health. She implemented a "green" policy that follows federally mandated LEED (Leadership in Energy and Environmental Design) standards for recycling and landfill sites. Dane County prohibits the sale of mercury thermometers, one of the first jurisdictions in the nation to do so. Phosphate fertilizers are banned from use on lawns. Storm water ordinances meant to reduce algae growth in the county's 37 lakes also include a rare thermal standard meant to protect trout streams. A $300,000 project converts methane, a byproduct of sewage treatment, to electricity. Protecting 2,500 farms in the county from development pressure requires strict land-use planning and zoning ordinances, which have the additional impact of restraining "white flight," a social and economic issue Madison prefers to avoid, unlike Detroit. Kathleen sees her leadership role as critical to getting the regulations right. With land-use planning, she is always aware that the county has just one opportunity to get it right.

As county executive, Kathleen springs into action whenever a crisis arises. When heavy rains threaten flooding along lakefronts, for example, she first holds a press conference to announce a "no wake" policy for boats and then assigns her emergency crews to work with volunteers to place sandbags along the shorelines if homes are at risk. Kathleen lives in a less-affluent neighborhood in Madison, and her home telephone number is listed in the directory. People approach her

Kathleen Falk announcing the proposed resolution restricting the use of phosphorus in lawn fertilizers (Dane County Board Supervisor Andy Olsen is on the left).

The Faces of Public Health, *Kathleen Falk*   33

With April Scheel, a volunteer at Yahara House, a nonprofit organization that partners with employers in the community to help those with mental illness.

Announcing the joint Centennial State Park / Dane County Lake Farm Park with Scott Hassett, secretary of the Wisconsin Dept. of Natural Resources.

On an interview.

With sisters Katie and Lizzie Hoeschler, winners of the bronze and silver medals in the women's logrolling championship, part of the ESPN Great Outdoor Games.

In her office with Bonnie Stronach, executive secretary.

wherever she goes, and she values these interactions. The proud mother of a grown son, Kathleen has been married twice. Peter Bock, her husband, served in the State Assembly for 16 years representing a district in Milwaukee. After he lost the seat due to redistricting, he served as the administrator of a state agency for one year under Governor Doyle before retiring from state service. He plans to teach history to middle school students.

Kathleen provides leadership on issues that affect the public's health. Thanks to generous private donations, Dane County has perhaps the best bike trail system in the nation, offering easy access to an exercise option that helps prevent obesity. Ozone buildup caused by traffic congestion and automobile emissions is a concern, especially for people with asthma. Kathleen would like to build a commuter rail system to lessen reliance on automobiles in Dane County and has turned to Ottawa, Europe and Japan for models of how this can be done. As with many creative approaches to serving the public interest, the challenge of how to finance new projects often requires the greatest creativity.

In her role as Dane County executive, Kathleen Falk, in essence, defends the right of citizens to participate in decisions that benefit the public interest. Her passionate defense of the right to a healthier environment is just one of the ways she fights for the public interest. She also promotes the rights of families to good health, exemplified by her 2004 Early Childhood Initiative. This initiative promotes a culture of hope and success for parents or caretakers and their young children. In tasking the county's public health nurses and other Human Services employees to intervene with young families, the initiative focuses on increasing family access to prenatal care and to developmental screening and assessment of infants, toddlers and young children. The initiative also promotes parenting education and support, immunizations and other appropriate health care, childcare and basic human needs assistance, and finally case management that provides training and self-sustaining employment. Kathleen understands that the interplay between health, education, employment and the environment is integral to the well-being of a community. She does everything in her power to persuade her constituents that these four elements, when in balance, become the foundation for healthy lives. She is proof that one person can make a difference in the fight for the public's health.

Kathleen's advice to people considering careers in public health is to remember that when you have your health, you have everything. She believes everyone shares the fundamental desire to be healthy and to stay healthy in a healthy environment. Everyone has a right to health. Working in public health gives the satisfaction of working on things we all value, Kathleen observes. As an educator, lawyer and policy-maker herself, she regards the potential of her skills set as unlimited and the opportunities these skills give her to make a difference as also unlimited. She hopes this sense of unlimited opportunity draws many new people to public health.

Looking ahead, Kathleen sees an explosion in diseases related to the environment, such as asthma, cancer and obesity, unless prevention wins equal billing with improved medications. Since these diseases worry people, she believes the public will demand a better set of decisions from their elected officials. She finds that while most people care, they do not know what to do. While some step up to help effect change, or simply vote, too many do nothing. As a public servant, her goal is to involve as many people as possible in reaching consensus solutions for seemingly intractable problems.

In her role as Dane County executive, building on her earlier experiences as Wisconsin's public intervenor fighting for public access to, and protection of, natural resources and as an environmental activist, Kathleen Falk shapes local government to be an instrument for responsive change. In her view, responsive change always promotes healthy lifestyles. In focusing on the public interest, the charge for all public officials, she improves both the built environment and open space in her county through inclusive land-use planning. She encourages constituents to participate in decision-making and to become advocates, like her, for responsible growth policies that will help ensure the public's health in a healthy environment.

Amy Forsyth-Stephens, MSW

Virginia

*Providing pro bono mental health services
for underserved communities*

Creativity and leadership count. By finding a way to bring free mental health services to a poor and underserved population, one woman was able to transform a local project into a national model. Amy Forsyth-Stephens, executive director of the Mental Health Association of New River Valley, Virginia, saw an opportunity to create a public-private partnership that serves the community in a visionary yet practical way.

Access to mental health services is a pressing issue for low-income, uninsured people. At some time in their lives, one in four Americans suffers mental health or substance abuse problems that need to be addressed by mental health professionals. Unfortunately, even for those with good health insurance plans, the reimbursement policies for mental health are unpredictable. For the uninsured, mental health services are difficult to find. In small rural communities with few mental health professionals nearby, the problem is even worse. By creating a program that provides mental health services for free to the low-income, uninsured community, Amy filled a huge health-care void in her area. Her innovative program, the Pro Bono Counseling Program, creates a "win-win" environment for both mental health professionals and the working poor.

Amy's first exposure to the struggles of the underserved came as a young girl growing up in Illinois. The youngest of four siblings, Amy was born in Olney, in the coal field country of southern Illinois. When she was eight the family moved from coal fields to pumpkin fields, relo-

cating to Morton, a small town in central Illinois 10 miles from Peoria. A pumpkin cannery owned by Libby's, the major industry in Morton, stood near Amy's new home. As she grew older, she became aware of the disparities in living conditions for the migrant workers she saw entering and leaving the plant. They lived in deplorable housing and lacked access to even basic health care. The migrant workers were largely invisible transients, and the town did not intervene to improve their plight.

When she was in high school, Amy took an "interest survey" that predicted she would be either a minister or a social worker. Thinking back on family history that may have influenced her choice of social work as a career, she remembers being told that her grandmother took in "hobos" throughout the Great Depression, providing food and shelter. More immediate was her discomfort at the plight of the migrant workers she saw entering and leaving the Libby's plant.

After graduating from Morton High School in 1975 near the top of her class, Amy enrolled at the University of Illinois Champaign-Urbana. She majored in psychology and graduated with honors in 1979. She studied with Michael G. H. Coles, renowned in the field of the psychology of learning, and wrote her senior thesis on "attribution theory" – the causes for why things happen, such as falling in love. She had personal experience in that regard, deciding to follow her boyfriend to Tallahassee after graduation when he enrolled in a doctoral program in clinical psychology. That boyfriend, Bob Stephens, is now her husband of 24 years. Amy enrolled in the two-year Master of Social Work (MSW) program at Florida State University, again graduating with honors with a perfect 4.0 grade point average. In 1982 she landed a dream job with the Florida State Department of Health and Rehabilitative Services.

Amy joined the Program Office for Alcohol, Drug Abuse and Mental Health and immediately put her MSW training in program evaluation to use. Assigned to monitor the office's de-institutionalized mental health programs, she monitored the closing of state psychiatric wards and the transitioning of patients to new community-based treatment systems throughout the state, called ARTS (Adult Residential and Treatment Systems) and GRTS (Geriatric Residential and Treatment Systems). Amy evaluated clients' success in progressing from group homes with 24-hour care to supervised apartments (usually four people and a supervisor) to satellite apartments that provided prevocational training. In preparing reports for delivery to the state legislature, Amy discovered that Florida's innovations in mental health services placed it on the cutting edge. Amy's exposure to state-level community innovation proved very valuable for the jobs that followed.

In 1984, Amy moved with her husband from Tallahassee to Seattle when he accepted a post-doctoral position at the University of Washington to research treatment of marijuana dependence. After the move, Amy joined a program to evaluate intensive case management (which she termed "Alley Therapy") for Seattle's homeless population. In doing so, she negotiated a joint position with the Division of Community Psychiatry at the University of Washington Medical Center and the King County Department of Human Resources Mental Health Section. This allowed Amy to leverage an academic powerhouse in helping a county improve its public mental health services. Two programs she helped implement – a new laundromat next door to the large homeless shelter in downtown Seattle, staffed with mental health professionals, and a jail diversion program, which placed parole officers and mental health case managers in the same office – improved services and outcomes for the homeless mentally ill.

In 1989, Amy took four years off to start a family that now includes three daughters. The family relocated from Seattle to Blacksburg, Virginia, when her husband became a professor of psychology at Virginia Tech, where he is a leading specialist on the treatment of marijuana dependence. In 1993, Amy decided to re-enter the work world and was appointed executive director of the Mental Health Association of New River Valley, Inc. Founded in 1965 by the Reverend Al Payne, a beloved person in the community whose son had a serious mental health problem, the association was a small nonprofit that focused on community education and advocacy. The annual budget at the time was $32,000 and the staff consisted of Amy and a part-time secretary.

Amy's goal as executive director was to instill Reverend Payne's ideals in her strategic planning and to expand the agency's services to become more need-based and outcome-oriented. She secured a six-year grant in 1998 from the Carilion Foundation, a private foundation serving southwestern Virginia, and then a three-year grant from the Virginia Health Care Foundation for 2000-2002. With the financial backing provided by these two grants, Amy created the nation's first-ever "free clinic for mental health" – the Pro Bono Counseling Program.

In order for mental health providers to devote part of their practice to serving those least able to afford their services, an obligation of their profession, they must either reduce their fees or provide free (pro bono) service. The managed care industry usually insists that fees not vary, however, as a condition of belonging to the provider network. Providers who vary fees within their practices, therefore, risk losing that affiliation.

However, if providers provide pro bono services under the auspices of a separate, nonprofit entity, they can satisfy insurance regulations and at the same time meet their obligations to the underserved. This is where the Pro Bono Counseling Program steps in.

Amy also saw another channel for increasing the pool of mental health professionals. To earn their licenses, students who earn master's degrees in counseling or social work must accrue a specified number of clinical face-to-face hours and clinical supervision hours. The Pro Bono Counseling Program offers a neat solution by providing both the legal organizational umbrella for mental health providers to meet their pro bono obligations and the supervised clinical setting trainees need to become licensed. Clients of the Pro Bono Counseling Program are seen within 10 days, while the insured can wait up to three months for appointments with therapists and up to five months with psychiatrists (only five psychiatrists serve New River Valley). In an ironic twist, Amy has given the uninsured more timely and accessible mental health services than are available to many of the insured.

Amy knows firsthand about the mental health needs of a rural population. In 2001, Amy learned that her brother had a serious mental health disorder – mania accompanied by a generalized anxiety disorder. He had been a loner all his life, and although family members had noticed bizarre behaviors and increasing isolation through the years, he had managed to hide the depths of his mental health disorder. By 2003, he had become dependent on benzodiazepines to control his escalating symptoms, had lost his job and everything he owned, and was one step away from a homeless shelter. As soon as the family became aware of his deepening plight, they intervened.

*With Jane Mahone,
at work staffing an
ARMS Reach client.*

*Amy with ARMS Reach
collaborator Dr. Jody
Hershey, director of New
River Health District and
president of the National
Association of County and
City Health Officials.*

All These People Are Wearing Masks.

In fact, they're wearing an invisible mask to cover up problems. That's how many people deal with mental health conditions – they don't.

Instead, they're afraid and they keep quiet, hoping it will get better.

You probably know someone who hides behind a mask because, in any given year, one out of five people need care for a mental health problem. These are problems such as depression, stress, anxiety, and obsessive compulsive disorders.

As with any other illness or injury, a mental health problem needs acknowledged and treated.

Today, most mental health conditions are treated effectively through therapy and prescription drug options.

Working together, we can help you feel better and live better. Call us at 1-800-559-2800 for more information.

We care.

DON'T HIDE FROM MENTAL HEALTH.

*Amy delivering irises (the
logo of the ARMS Reach
program) and information
about the program.*

*"Sandy the Ostrich" is the official
mascot of the agency's anti-stigma
campaign. Sandy says, "Don't Hide
from Mental Health!"*

They moved their brother from Mississippi to Indiana, where he lives near Amy's sister, a registered nurse, and receives rehabilitative and vocational services through a mental health clubhouse program.

In 2002, Amy collaborated with Dr. Jody Hershey, director of the New River Health District of the Virginia State Department of Health, to begin planning an ambitious new program, *ARMS Reach*: Access to Rural Mental Health Services. Their brainchild would seek to break down remaining access barriers to the Pro Bono Counseling Program, such as transportation and stigma. The Pro Bono Counseling Program is based in Blacksburg and located centrally in the New River District. Aside from the population centers of Blacksburg and Radford, both university towns, the district serves four largely rural counties. The counties each have a health department, as does the city of Radford, all under the supervision of Dr. Hershey's New River Health District. Blacksburg itself has a permanent population of 20,000 and 24,000 students enrolled at Virginia Tech.

Among numerous grants secured by Amy over the years, the most recent came in 2003 from the U.S. Health Resources and Services Administration (HRSA) for $600,000 over three years. Earmarked for rural mental health outreach, the grant enabled Amy and Dr. Hershey to make *ARMS Reach* a reality. The project doubled the overall number of trainees, placing them in a variety of community settings convenient for rural residents and free from the stigma that can keep people from seeking professional mental health care. Prescriptions, free to the patients, are also covered through the grant. Amy likens the *ARMS Reach* project to *Stone Soup*, the children's story. In the story, a hungry villager with no food

begins boiling water in a cauldron in the center of the village and implores each villager to contribute one carrot or one onion or one potato. With each villager contributing the little they can, the cauldron soon bubbles with a rich soup, enough to feed the whole village.

Amy advises young people entering the public health field to seek solutions that may seem obvious but are daunting due to red tape. The trick is to creatively address and dissect problems, cutting through red tape to come up with solutions. When solutions gain consensus from the community, they work. In Amy's own experience at the Mental Health Association of New River Valley, what started as a band-aid grew into a sling and then into a cast. Mental health providers worked with a population never served previously to prevent problems from escalating into life crises, fostering job productivity and parenting success in the process. In the New River Health District, 83 percent of the population that needs mental health care now has access, and fully 63 percent of those served complete the full course of treatment. These are remarkable outcomes for mental health, especially for a largely rural corner of Virginia.

In anticipating the future of mental health, Amy foresees an ongoing wave of privatization in care and an increasing dominance of psychotropic drugs in treatment. States seem to be getting out of the mental health business, but if government creates the right incentives and if reimbursement rates are adequate, the future of mental health services could be bright. Insurance reimbursement is the key issue – with proper coverage, free clinics would no longer be needed and everyone who needs mental health services would have access regardless of the type of insurance. Amy would like nothing better than

to be able to cut off the cast – free clinics for the uninsured – and make reliable mental health services available equally to everyone.

From her beginnings in the coal field country of Illinois and her later awareness of the plight of migrant workers in the pumpkin fields, Amy Forsyth-Stephens focused in her work on making mental health services accessible to the underserved, especially the rural poor. She sought practical solutions, secured grants from private and public foundations, collaborated in private-public partnerships and cultivated government as her staunchest ally. Her unstinting commitment to people least able to help themselves makes Amy Forsyth-Stephens an exemplar of the public health professional.

Ron Graves, DDS

Oklahoma

Taking a stand on anti-smoking legislation

Not all public health professionals begin their public health careers straight out of school. Dr. Ron Graves, immediate past president and current member of the Oklahoma State Board of Health, has had a successful practice in oral and maxillofacial surgery in Ardmore, Oklahoma, for more than 20 years. In his surgical practice, while treating maxillofacial injuries and jaw deformities, he felt the satisfaction of improving the lives of patients, one person at a time. He also served as chief of staff at the leading hospital in Ardmore. Only after he reluctantly agreed to serve on the State Board of Health in 1998 to fill an unexpired term did his career in public health begin. Despite his worries about the major commitment of time away from his practice, public health won him over. In waging a battle to legislate smoke-free public spaces in Oklahoma, Dr. Graves witnessed firsthand how enlightened policies could sway behavior and how prevention could promote healthier populations.

Ron Graves was born and raised in Clinton, Oklahoma, a town of 10,000 people known as the "Hub City of Western Oklahoma." As a student at Southwestern Oklahoma State College, Ron intended to be a pre-medicine major. However, his best friend and college roommate was a pre-dental student, and urged him to switch majors.

Back in Clinton, Ron interviewed local dentists and doctors to determine the relative merits of a career in dentistry or medicine. He decided dentistry would offer him a more stable family life and made the switch. After graduation, Ron headed to the School of Dentistry at the University of Missouri in Kansas City (UMKC) to train for family dentistry.

Graduating from UMKC with his dentistry degree in 1970 during the later stages of the Vietnam War, Ron enlisted in the U.S. Army. He was posted to the Red Stone Arsenal in Huntsville, Alabama, for a two-year tour of duty. The oral surgeons on staff immediately enlisted him to assist in their busy practice, and he quickly became hooked on their specialty. Due to the special teaching skills of one particular mentor, Dr. John Miller, Ron switched his career focus to oral and maxillofacial surgery.

At the end of his two-year stint in Alabama, Ron began a three-year training program in oral and maxillofacial surgery at the Oklahoma University Medical Center in Oklahoma City. With his training complete, Ron and his wife, whom he had married before his senior year in college, carefully considered their options for work and family, and chose to raise their two children in Ardmore. In this affluent and stable community of 30,000 people near the Texas border, Ron established himself over two decades as a leading oral surgeon.

When the governor recruited Ron to join the State Board of Health, the "State of the State's Health Report" ranked Oklahoma 44th to 47th in the nation in most health indicators. This very low ranking resulted from poor lifestyle choices. The Board believed Oklahomans could and should fare better, and set out systematically to improve the state's standing.

Tobacco use became the Board's first focus. A 1999 review of data for the previous 10 years showed that the growth in cases of chronic obstructive pulmonary disease (COPD), also called emphysema, had ballooned 27 percent in Oklahoma compared to only 9 percent growth in the nation overall. During the same period, California experienced a 1 percent decline in COPD, a dramatic difference and an eye-opener to policy-makers in Oklahoma. They attributed the disparate results to the restrictive smoke-free laws that California had enforced for a decade.

In Oklahoma, exposure to tobacco use, often as secondhand smoke, wreaked havoc on people, most notably children. Its consequences were the leading cause of preventable death, with no close second. Deaths from motor vehicle accidents, gunshot wounds, alcohol abuse, homicides and suicides, combined, amounted to fewer deaths. Roughly 750 nonsmokers were dying each year from exposure to secondhand smoke, approximately 2,250 infants were afflicted each year with bronchitis and pneumonia caused by secondhand smoke, and 12,000 children suffered from severe bouts of asthma each year. In addition, an estimated 300,000 to 400,000 workers in Oklahoma were subjected frequently to secondhand smoke in the workplace.

Ron is proud of the way he and his colleagues on the Oklahoma State Board of Health worked to win broad support to create smoke-free public spaces in the state. Oklahoma has always been a tough nut to crack with regard to tobacco, with state legislators unusually amenable to the interests of tobacco lobbyists and the restaurant industry, which feared restrictive anti-smoking laws. The law on the books, a half-hearted attempt called the "Smoking in Public Places Act," did not allow for strict regulation of secondhand smoke in hospitals, restaurants and most other public places. In addition, the law was "preemptive," which meant that no local government in the state could pass stricter regulations.

Under Ron's leadership, the State Board of Health set out to make an immediate difference in the lives of Oklahoma's 3.4 million people. Working with the State Department of Health, which helped draft legislative language, carried out policies and developed initiatives, the Board members cultivated relationships with legislative subcommittees, collected and analyzed data, and switched from a reactive to a proactive role. Although smoke-free legislation had always died in committee, the authorizing legislation for the Board actually allowed it to adopt rule-making that would have the force of law. This meant that the Board's rules could stand as laws if the governor approved them, unless the legislature overruled them. Even if the legislature rolled back the rules, policy issues were at least debated publicly rather than being bottled up in committee.

In March 2002 the Board, under Ron's leadership, ruled that smoking should be banned in virtually all public places and workplaces statewide. Ron had the unanimous agreement of his fellow members of the State Board of Health in this effort – Haskell Evans, Jr., RPh (vice president), Glen Discon, Jr., MD, Jay Gregory, MD, Ann Warn, MD, Gordon Deckert, MD, John Carmichael, DDS, Dan Fieker, DO, and Ron Ousterhout. At first, the governor approved only rules that addressed smoking in health care facilities. Little did the governor anticipate that the public would swamp his switchboard with calls supporting the full sweep of the rules.

With no direct funding, the Board could merely represent the moral high ground and strive to win public support. Fortunately, the state's professional associations representing various medical specialties had already passed their own resolutions supporting smoke-free legislation. The associations now banded together to fund a media campaign in support of the rules, encouraging their collective membership to start a letter-writing campaign to state legislators. At the same time, a major hospital system sent letters to the editor and position papers to local newspapers. Universities committed their political science departments to do polling, which showed overwhelming public support for the rules. The poll results gained widespread coverage in the press. As momentum built, editorials by the newspapers themselves supported the rules and helped elevate the issue progressively until it became the focus of the legislature.

In April 2002, the governor urged the legislature to immediately adopt legislation banning smoking in all public places, including restaurants. He said if they failed to do so, he would work with the Board of Health after the legislative session adjourned to develop strong rules that he would sign. In May 2002, the public outcry for action resulted in the legislature adopting a limited measure to make state-owned buildings smoke-free.

As promised, the governor worked closely with the Board of Health to develop "emergency rules" that were adopted and signed in June 2002. Those rules were immediately challenged in court, extending the publicity and editorial comments. Separate legal actions by the State Department of Health and by third parties were taken in response to lawsuits supported by the Oklahoma Restaurant Association. The gathering storm of phone calls, letter-writing, editorials and negative media attention led the Oklahoma Restaurant Association to reverse course, however,

With nurse Jamie Vernon.

Dr. Graves consults with Dr. Leslie Beitsch, JD, former Commissioner of Health, in the boardroom at the Oklahoma State Board of Health.

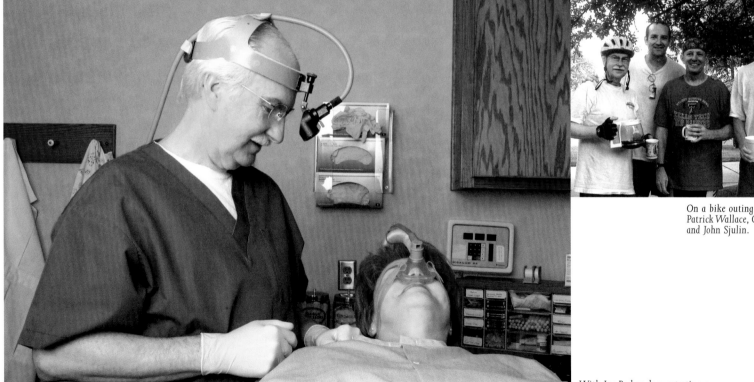

On a bike outing with doctors Patrick Wallace, Gerald Cross, and John Sjulin.

With Joy Parker, demonstrating a maxillofacial surgery consultation.

and call for all public places to be smoke-free. In fact, the latest member to be appointed to the State Board of Health is a restaurant owner.

The Board continued to focus attention on clean indoor air by adopting more rules in March 2003, simultaneously urging final adoption of clean indoor air measures that were steadily progressing through the legislature. The coordinated advocacy efforts paid off in May 2003, when the legislature finally adopted the rules in full and for the first time enacted meaningful, restrictive smoke-free legislation. Restaurants in Oklahoma will have until 2006 to phase in the law's requirements, which became effective on September 1, 2003.

Ron's tenure on the Oklahoma State Board of Health was extended in 2002 when the governor appointed him to a standard nine-year term. He worked closely at that time with Dr. Leslie Beitsch, appointed by the Board as State Health Commissioner. As Assistant Health Commissioner in Florida prior to his appointment, Dr. Beitsch witnessed the power of initiatives to change unhealthy behavior. In Oklahoma, he adopted the Board's agenda and became a key advocate, influencing the legislature and building broad public support.

With its goal of improving the quality of indoor air in Oklahoma accomplished, the State Board of Health has turned its focus to reducing death tolls from cardiovascular disease, cancer and diabetes. To do this, Oklahomans must address obesity, rising levels of physical inactivity and poor lifestyle choices in the same way they addressed smoke-free legislation. Only with broad public support for healthy behaviors will public health be elevated across the state.

Dr. Graves believes the bioterrorism threat that arose after September 11, 2001, shook an otherwise complacent public, lulled by an absence of health crises in their ongoing lives. The public takes for granted safe drinking water, clean air and effective vaccines, advances that without question have a beneficial impact on daily life. The quest for healthy choices never ends, however. Increased resources for public health will be needed, and fortunately, the public's growing appreciation of the role of public health in their lives should encourage an increase in resources in the future.

Through his own example, becoming the head of Oklahoma's State Board of Health late in his career, Dr. Ron Graves proves that it is never too late to begin to make an impact on healthy choices for a population. Advances in public health depend on broad support from the public and leadership from unexpected sources.

Chris Hoke, JD

North Carolina

Leading the nation in public health law reform

One man's boredom is another man's passion. So discovered Chris Hoke, a lawyer by training, who has thrived for more than two decades in a public health career that his predecessor thought would not challenge an honors graduate from UNC Law School. A lifelong North Carolinian, Chris was able to fuse his background in law with the ever-evolving challenges of public health. His energy, enthusiasm and intelligence are well-known throughout his state, and he is recognized as leading the nation in public health law reform. Born with a mild physical handicap and growing up in the South during the turbulent civil rights era, Chris has overcome various obstacles by letting the force of his positive personality shine through.

Chris currently serves as chief deputy to the State Health Director in the Division of Public Health of the North Carolina State Department of Health and Human Services. In addition, Chris is chief of the Office of Regulatory and Legal Affairs. He came to public health purely by chance, responding to a job posting on the UNC Law School bulletin board. Ironically, the job's incumbent — a classmate at UNC Law School moving on to a law firm — warned him the job would be boring. Not so. Since starting the job in late 1980, Chris has never looked back.

Chris was born in Taylorsville in the Great Smoky Mountain foothills in western North Carolina. Both his father and his mother (who is now deceased), were born and raised in Taylorsville where his father lives today. His father, a civil engineer who designed and built water and sewage treatment plants, moved the family to Durham shortly after Chris was born. Chris is the third of four boys, with the youngest born 14 years later. Of the brothers, all of whom are lifelong North Carolinians, only Chris found his way to public health.

Chris attended Durham High School, an almost exclusively white school, in his freshman and sophomore years. As a junior, in the midst of countywide integration, he was transferred to Hillside High School, a previously all-black school closer to home. The experience of fitting into a new environment in a school that was 65 percent black taught him valuable life lessons. Facing the trauma of change and wondering how the ice could be broken, Chris discovered that the black students, more secure in their environment, reached out first. Chris soon grew to love his new school, learning to get along with new people and respect differences. He made a new set of friends and considered himself lucky to have a second set at home. He joined a newly created golf team, a team beyond his reach at his old school, and golfed for free at the local public course. He was fortunate that a young and energetic math teacher pushed the higher-achieving students with her motto, "do more, don't set your sights low."

Chris chose to attend the University of North Carolina in nearby Chapel Hill, holding open visits home to Durham often enough to eat home-cooked meals, do his laundry and root for the Duke basketball team from courtside. He intended to concentrate on math and science courses, his strengths in high school, but also took courses in psychology and the religion of the ancient Middle East that delighted him and expanded his mind. Venturing beyond his known strengths, he double-majored in psychology and religion, wanting to learn as much as he could about life and what makes people tick. He grew his hair long and confounded his parents with his choice of majors. During the summers, he installed water mains and sewage pipes at large construction sites and honed his physical conditioning.

A huge sports fan, Chris continued to accompany his father to Duke University basketball games once he enrolled at UNC Chapel Hill. To this day, he keeps his family's season tickets, now joined by his 16-year-old son. Although he took much ribbing from his Tarheel classmates for supporting a team that in those years never made a title run, his avid support of Duke basketball has paid dividends in recent years.

In his senior year Chris applied to six graduate programs in clinical psychology and was accepted by none – a disappointment to the hard-working student. UNC alone had 1,200 applications for four places. Fortunately, he followed his father's advice and applied at the same time to UNC Law School, where he was accepted off the waiting list. He didn't think of himself as a law student, but his father assured him that his love of argument would take him far.

The first year of law school shook his self-confidence. Chris had neither immediate nor extended family involved in the law, while students with family ties to the law surrounded

him. The other students were highly competitive, seeming to thrive on the Socratic teaching method that he found intimidating. One three-hour final exam determined the grade in each course; at one point he approached his contract law professor and asked, "What do I do not to flunk out?" The professor gave him no guidance he could effectively use and Chris dreaded more and more that he didn't quite fit, that law school wasn't for him. Much to his surprise, he achieved the highest grade in his class in contract law. He read twice through the posted grade list, starting at the bottom and getting no further than the Cs, before he realized his Social Security number was at the top with an A. He managed the same feat in his corporate tax course.

As it turned out, Chris enjoyed what he was learning in law school. The skills fit his strengths – analyzing, thinking and seeing all sides of an issue. Although he started out not knowing where he stood, he soon realized law school was a good fit. He graduated with honors with a 3.4 GPA and made *Law Review*.

Chris was born with a mild case of cerebral palsy (CP), and after graduating from law school, he found it difficult to find a job in a law firm. A medium-sized firm in Charlotte invited him for follow-up interviews, but a partner leveled with him that it would be difficult for someone with CP to find a position in any firm. In the years before the Americans With Disabilities Act (ADA), law firms worried that clients might feel uncomfortable dealing with a lawyer with a disability. Firms also worried that securing health insurance might pose a problem. The partner recommended that Chris look for a government position instead, specifically with the IRS.

Chris worked for six months building a water treatment plant while he continued to search for work as a lawyer. The job involved working outdoors for 10 hours a day, even in winter. Chris developed his first appreciation for public health through the knowledge he gained about water treatment and also gained a healthy respect for people who work outdoors. At the same time, he kept his hand in the law by working part time for a lawyer in Durham who was a state legislator.

A 3- by 5-inch card on a bulletin board at the law school advertising a position at the State Division of Public Health opened the door to public health for Chris. The posting sought an attorney to do rule-making. He applied, interviewed, and was hired for the entry-level position in late December 1980. The incumbent, a law school classmate moving on to a law firm, told Chris he would not find the job challenging, remembering that Chris had made *Law Review*. In concentrating on how he could contribute to the organization, however, Chris discovered that the job provided plenty of opportunities and challenges. When he asked the Deputy State Health Director, Dr. Ron Levine, "What's my role?" he answered, "Whatever you make of it." Dr. Levine went on to become State Health Director and served for 17 years. He advised, "Be a bulldog. Never be satisfied, but get what you can. At times this will be quick, at other times painfully slow."

Chris pulled together a task force of lawyers from the attorney general's office, the legislature and the Institute of Government to tackle the existing public health laws, many of which were archaic. Although he was the youngest on the team, he took the leadership role and was fortunate that his colleagues were collegial and public-spirited. Together, through three years of hard work, they recodified the public health laws, writing a new chapter to bring the laws up to standard. For example, the new chapter replaced a maximum $50 fine as the criminal penalty for violation of a public health rule with a maximum penalty of two years in jail and an unlimited fine. The new chapter added numerous flexible remedies such as embargo, civil or administrative monetary penalties, suspension or revocation of permits, recovery of money and forfeiture of gain.

The task force anticipated future developments as well. To address threats to the public's health that may not be addressed by a specific health law or rule, the new chapter added abatement of public health nuisances and abatement of imminent hazards. The hog farms that caused widespread pollution of the water supply during the floods of 2002 were an example in North Carolina. The work was painstaking, requiring the group to push boundaries and recommend laws that would be both comprehensive and adaptable to changing circumstances. The North Carolina Legislature addressed the task force recommendations in 1983. After many donnybrooks in committee and on the floor, the legislature enacted the new chapter of public health law to take effect on the first day of 1984.

Chris points to the law on graduated driving licenses as an example of how sound public health policy changes society for the better. In North Carolina, regulations governing the age at which teenagers can drive independently – accompanied by an adult at first, no night driving second, etc. – have saved many lives. He loves how public health looks at data, analyzes it, finds out what needs to be done, then designs a law for public health intervention that leads to real, quantifiable improvements in the quality of life. There are times, however, when the public health community needs to act before all the answers are known.

The *Pfiesteria piscicida* controversy in North Carolina was one such occasion. These periodic but short-lived toxic outbreaks in polluted coastal

At a meeting discussing the North Carolina public health system.

With assistant Carla Moore.

With North Carolina State Health Director Leah Devlin.

waters are fatal to large quantities of fish but pose little threat to human health. The press presented conjectures as facts, however, making it seem that the public health authorities were not leveling with the public about possible harm. In response, state agencies involved with the water supply, including the Division of Public Health, stressed even more convincingly that scientific studies had yet to show any threat to humans. Since humans did not in fact suffer any ill effects during the outbreaks, the controversy died down in time. As Chris points out, "We don't have much in public health, but we do have our credibility. We need to guard it carefully."

In the late 1980s, North Carolina revisited the public health laws to recodify selective statutes in light of HIV/AIDS and other communicable diseases. Since September 11, 2001, the laws have been revisited yet again to address the issue of bioterrorism. The anthrax incident in Florida, which touched on North Carolina, demonstrated that gaps in the laws as they were then written needed to be closed with new approaches to surveillance before harm could become widespread. In 2004, North Carolina plans to revisit the laws once again in light of Toronto's experience with SARS. As Chris points out, consensus among public health emergency responders is critical. Responders to a crisis should agree on one approach because if the media detect even one difference, they will magnify it and make controversy the whole story.

Since 1993 Chris has sat on the management committee of the Association of State and Territorial Health Officials (ASTHO), addressing national issues by thinking strategically and sharing his knowledge of what is possible in his own state. Chris recently participated in the CDC's second annual conference on the law and public health.

Attracting participants from the offices of attorney generals at the state and federal levels as well as all levels of public health, the conference acknowledges the growing role of legal affairs in shaping fundamental decisions about how public health departments interact with the public through such activities as surveillance, data reporting and quarantine. Chris enjoys his work with ASTHO and the legal side of public health and finds that working on national issues keeps him active and fresh.

Chris has found public health to be a wonderful, fulfilling and challenging career. His office usually hires a summer intern, sometimes from law school, sometimes from an MPH program, and he finds it rewarding to strike a chord in another person and engage them in public policy debates and public management decisions. For young, smart people, public health and its constant challenges afford the ability to make a huge impact. New, unexpected twists and turns, such as SARS, or the obesity epidemic, or a new bioterrorism threat, always lurk around the corner.

As for the future of public health, Chris allows that he's an optimist. He sees public health continuing to play a vital role in society, especially since the events following September 11 reinforced that role with policy-makers and the public. He thinks growth at the local level will be hard and foresees a greater role for public health at the national level, with increases in funding leading to greater success.

Chris Hoke takes pride in all that he has accomplished for North Carolinians during his public health career. As a lifelong North Carolinian, he is delighted that his oversight of the state's public health laws has improved the lives of everyone in his state.

Ted Holloway, MD

Georgia

Enhancing child and teen health with DAISY

The Quechuan people of Bolivia and the citizens of southeast Georgia share someone in common — Dr. John Teddy Holloway. Dr. Holloway, known as Ted, found his calling as a public health professional in the Bolivian jungle and carried that commitment with him to the rural corner of Georgia he has served since 1974.

In the summer of 1966, after graduating from Wofford College as a history major and before his first year at the Medical College of South Carolina in Charleston, Ted traveled to Bolivia and ended up providing basic health services to villagers in the remote interior. His experiences in the jungle showed him how access to care and information improved the lives of individual patients and, even more impressively, of an entire population. Ted's experiences in Bolivia led him to rethink his future in medicine and undertake an unanticipated career path – public health.

In Bolivia, purely by chance, Ted met Dr. Jim Alley at a jungle clinic in Montero. Dr. Alley, an unconventional Methodist missionary, had transformed a jungle clinic over 10 years into a state-of-the-art medical facility. The clinic primarily served the Quechuan people, a population that had been relocated by the Bolivian government to plots of land in the jungle to become subsistence farmers. Unfortunately, these native people began to succumb to diseases

for which they had no natural immunity, an unintended consequence of their relocation from highland homes. This challenging situation and environment served as Ted's first exposure to public health.

Ted returned to the Bolivian jungle clinic during the winter of his final year in medical school. He set up one-day clinics in remote villages to provide basic health care services and preventive health screenings. He treated fractures that had been improperly set and screened for tuberculosis and a host of other endemic diseases. He encountered infants dying from tetanus, the result of a local custom of binding a large, usually unclean, coin over the umbilical cord. Changing this custom alone reduced the rate of infant death by half.

Most revealing of all to the young medical student was a measles epidemic that threatened the local community. Ted watched Dr. Alley work within the customs and culture of the Quechuans as he rushed to inoculate the population and halt the outbreak. Dr. Alley found support in native healers trusted by the community – *los curanderos* – who he had trained to recognize diseases and refer the sickest patients to the clinic for treatment. In addition, he set up preceptor programs to train local physicians in specialty care.

Ted learned about epidemiology through another of Dr. Alley's creative ideas. Dr. Alley enlisted the students in the local high school to collect and analyze health statistics, an activity he built into the school's curriculum. The clinic doctors could then initiate medical interventions based on these findings. Ted learned firsthand that working within the customs and beliefs of a specific population, while encouraging the participation of its members, had a dramatic impact on the overall health of that community.

Ted left Bolivia and returned to Charleston to earn his medical degree. During a one-year rotating internship in Phoenix, Arizona, he met his wife, Linda, a nurse and trained social worker; they married in 1971. After two and a half years in the Navy, where Ted served as a medical officer and attended submarine school, he and Linda were lured to Waycross, Georgia. They answered the call of Dr. Alley, who had been named director of the Georgia Division of Public Health by the newly elected governor, Jimmy Carter. Knowing the public health calling his protégé had found in Bolivia, Dr. Alley appointed Ted to run the Southeast Health Unit.

Since Ted assumed his duties in 1974, the Southeast Health Unit has had a relatively stable population, growing from 290,000 to 320,000. However, an influx of immigrants from Latin America, mostly from Mexico, has made the area's demographics much more diverse. Vidalia onions were first planted in the early 1980s and quickly became the dominant agricultural commodity, attracting migrant laborers. The area's other major industries – chicken processing, small manufacturing, construction and distribution centers – rely equally on immigrant labor. Many of the district's new residents are undocumented and do not qualify for Medicaid, and Ted estimates that 25 percent of the adult population has no medical insurance. Access to high quality health care for all members of the district ranks as the top challenge Ted confronts, and he has worked tirelessly to build public health programs to meet the needs of every person.

Ted has tripled the number of full-time public health employees in his district to 450, a testament to his vision and ability to fund innovative programs. The staff works in 25 offices in 16 counties, close to the communities they serve. One of the hurdles many public health professionals face is funding for their programs. Ted learned the important lesson that the work of a public health professional often goes beyond the direct health service aspects of the job, and he became a creative advocate for his community and a policy-maker. Ted's district secures its funding from a mix of sources – 30 percent from the state, 20 percent from the counties, and the rest from the hospitals, federal government and private foundation grants, fees and Medicaid.

Creativity and innovation are Ted's signatures. Foremost among the innovative programs he has introduced is the DAISY program. Established in 1984, DAISY stands for Diversified Agencies Involved in Serving Youth. Ted saw the need for adolescents to seek preventive health care in privacy, and he conceived a "teen friendly" setting with all services under one roof. A variety of state agencies collaborate to provide medical doctors, psychologists, special education teachers and employment counselors, among others, to treat the customary problems of adolescence. Physicians treat sexually transmitted diseases and prescribe birth control. Psychologists treat depression and emotional and physical abuse. Social workers encourage pregnant teenagers to stay in school and help young mothers continue school by finding suitable day care. Special education teachers help handicapped youth make progress.

The Robert Wood Johnson (RWJ) Foundation initially funded the DAISY program for five years, at $250,000 per year, the result of a "concept paper" a visiting RWJ vice president encouraged Ted to write. The program continues beyond its five-year grant thanks to Ted's persistence in lobbying the state legislature. He managed to secure a direct annual allocation from the legislature that keeps the program fully funded.

As successful initiatives often lay the groundwork for other programs, the DAISY program led to the creation of the Family Connection Community Partnership Initiative, which now reaches 148 of Georgia's 159 counties. The Waycross/Ware County pilot site in Ted's district is considered a definitive model of health services for children.

Ted's foresight can be seen in a variety of other initiatives that provide access to health care and education for the people of southeast Georgia. He designed programs that use different approaches to reach the diverse populations within his district. For example, to ensure access to preventive health messages and screenings for children and teens, he developed a school nurse program. The first school health clinic opened at Waycross High School in 1987; grants from the RWJ Foundation and the Whitehead Foundation helped establish four additional school-based health clinics throughout the district. In addition, school nurses who have been trained in a pioneering certification program established within the Southeast Health Unit are based at 16 schools throughout the district. As Ted points out, it makes sense to bring health services to where the students are.

The Southeast Health Unit provides care to over 500 people living with HIV/AIDS each year. Ted's first challenge in the late 1980s was overcoming the common perception that HIV/AIDS was a disease of large urban environments. In 1989, Ted formed a consortium to combat HIV/AIDS in rural communities, and he fought to gain public recognition that the disease affects the rural poor too. His wife Linda helped establish a support network in the greater Waycross area for people with the disease, and the Southeast Health Unit has become known as a rural model for HIV/AIDS intervention.

Ted, far right, on a canoe trip in the Okefenokee Swamp with friends.

Fishing with his grandchild, Jay.

Driving a tractor on the family farm.

Ted with children at Children's Medical Services Clinic.

Recognizing that Georgia's nearest large specialty medical centers were in Savannah and Augusta, more than 100 miles from his district, Ted pioneered the use of telemedicine in the state. Thanks again to Ted's persistence, the Medical College of Georgia in Augusta installed telemedicine equipment in the Ware County Health Department in Waycross to allow specialty health consultations for local residents. The health district currently provides more telemedicine visits than the rest of Georgia combined. Telemedicine consultations improve the care given to HIV/AIDS patients, children with developmental delays, and patients with chronic conditions.

Maternal and child health is an important issue for any public health professional, and Ted is no exception. He understood that improving perinatal care requires a coordinated approach involving all aspects of sexual health and pregnancy. The Southeast Health Unit's perinatal program is a seamless, coordinated effort. It reduces STDs among teens and young sexually active women, improves access to prenatal care for low-income women and immigrants who do not qualify for Medicaid and educates expectant mothers on proper prenatal care to avoid low-birth-weight babies. Regarded as a model for the state, the program has successfully reduced infant mortality and improved maternal, infant and child health. Ted's vision for telemedicine also plays a role in this program: a new telemedicine service, Perinatal Health Partners, allows for real-time ultrasounds to be performed on high-risk obstetrics patients, and the images are read by a regional perinatalogist 160 miles away.

It is no surprise Ted chose health care as his profession. Ted's great-grandfather, grandfather and father were physicians, as are his two older brothers. Ted's father, William Jordan Holloway, established a rural practice in Ware Shoals, South Carolina, after graduating from the Medical College of South Carolina in Charleston. From the time he was five years old, Ted accompanied his father on house calls and always knew he wanted to become a physician.

His lifelong call to medicine evolved in the Bolivian jungle into a career in public health that has spanned 30 years and shows no signs of slowing down. Since Ted joined the Georgia Division of Public Health in 1974, every citizen in his rural corner of Georgia, an area the size of Massachusetts, has been touched by his uncanny ability to stretch scant resources, implement new programs, and fund them for the long haul.

While some may question whether they could devote a lifetime to one community, Ted's life and work have shown forcefully that it is not one's location or resources that are limiting, just one's imagination. He has used his creativity and ingenuity to bring the highest level of health care to his community, and has learned how to work within the culture and structure of his district to develop successful programs. From the Quechuan people of Bolivia to the residents of southeast Georgia, Ted Holloway has changed the lives of those around him for the better.

Paul Juarez, PhD

California

*Working to stop the cycle of
youth violence*

Youth violence has been a plague in America's inner cities, and Paul Juarez has been at the forefront in trying to remedy it. In Los Angeles, California, where Paul lived and worked, youth violence outranked diseases and accidental injuries as the leading cause of death among young men and women aged 20 to 24. Working in a hospital trauma center one harrowing weekend, Paul saw families camped out the length of the corridors waiting to hear if their sons would survive gunshot wounds and other intentional injuries. Learning that no counseling assistance was offered to these families during a stressful time, Paul realized he could use his background in public health and psychology to make a difference in their lives.

Paul co-founded two organizations in Los Angeles that address youth violence and its ramifications: Loved Ones of Homicide Victims (LOHV) and the Violence Prevention Coalition (VPC) of Greater Los Angeles. LOHV, the first grief-counseling support network in Los Angeles, broke a barrier in building awareness among law enforcement agencies that youth violence should also be treated as a crisis in public health. VPC promoted prevention strategies by bringing together community-based programs, law enforcement agencies, public health providers, schools, government agencies and the media. These diverse stakeholders collaborate as a coalition in employing public health strategies to lessen youth violence. While youth violence continues to claim lives in Greater Los Angeles, it no longer outranks other diseases or injuries as the leading cause of death, a testament to the work of Paul Juarez and his colleagues.

Paul Juarez was born in 1953 in Sunnyside, Washington, in the state's Yakima Valley. Although his ancestors were from Mexico, his grandparents on both sides were born in Texas and moved to the Yakima Valley as farm laborers, joining a large Latino emigration to the area. When he was in fourth grade, Paul's family moved to Bothell, a Seattle suburb, where he attended public school and graduated from Inglemoor High School in 1971. He attended Bellevue Community College for one and half years and transferred to Western Washington State University in Bellingham. He majored in psychology with a social psychology emphasis and graduated with a bachelor's degree in 1975. Western Washington fostered an interdisciplinary approach in large lecture sections, tying together anthropology, psychology and sociology, a highlight of Paul's undergraduate experience. Paul stayed on to earn a master's degree in educational psychology.

Paul's mentor at Western Washington, professor Walter Lonner, editor of the *Journal of Cross-Cultural Psychology*, asked Paul to join a research project in Tikul in the Yucatan Peninsula in Mexico. Happy to oblige, Paul spent the year before he started his master's degree program conducting community-based studies to assess how Mayan women in these rural communities depend on cues from their environment for perception and cognition. The Mayan women he tested wove huge hammocks with intricate patterns, none predetermined, and it turned out they were astonishingly adept at perceiving cues independent of their environment, thus disproving Witkin's cognitive differentiation theory. Paul

points to his experience among the Mayans as setting him on a course in life to question accepted norms. His time in Tikul also made him acutely aware that people may respond to their surrounding environment in ways hard to predict.

After earning his master's degree, Paul's first job was as a school counselor in the Yakima School District, working in a migrant education program at Davis High School. Eight months later he left, frustrated by his overloaded classroom and what he perceived as the school district's lack of commitment to the program. He then worked in a juvenile corrections program in Yakima, primarily with youth of Mexican American and Yakima Indian heritage. Gilbert Lusero, a professor at the University of Washington School of Social Work, became a mentor in this job. A nontraditional and controversial academic, Lusero encouraged graduate students he had brought to the Yakima Valley for practicum experience to organize lettuce boycotts and engage in other forms of social activism. Lusero instilled in Paul the notion that sometimes you need to break traditions and find new ways to advocate for change, a style adopted by Paul in his own work that has helped him influence solutions to public health problems in Los Angeles.

After two years working in juvenile corrections, and taking Lusero's advice, Paul completed applications to doctorate programs before heading off to Mexico in his camper truck. He was able to stretch his limited resources while he traveled the length of Mexico, from Baja to Chiapas, connecting with his roots. Learning of acceptances to the University of Michigan and Brandeis University upon his return, he headed straight to Ann Arbor, stopping just long enough to change his mind and continue on to Brandeis in the Boston suburbs. Arriving at Brandeis, he was

warmly greeted and made to feel welcome by the matriarchs of the Admissions Office, Fran Rosen and Fran Hahn. He decided to start the doctoral program in social policy and would spend the next three years at Brandeis.

Paul's key mentors at Brandeis were Gunnar Dybwad and his wife, Rosemary, who, like Gilbert Lusero, were nontraditional academics and often chose to take the road least traveled. They were renowned for their work in developmental disabilities, having innovated community-based care models. The Dybwads were also highly regarded for their advocacy work. Paul met his wife, Patricia Matthews Juarez, at Brandeis. A fellow social policy doctorate candidate, with an emphasis on mental health, she defended her dissertation on the same day as Paul. After graduation in 1983, they headed to Los Angeles, raising two daughters who are both now in college. Patricia has been affiliated with Charles R. Drew University (initially the Charles R. Drew Post-Graduate Medical School) since their arrival in Los Angeles.

Paul's first position in Los Angeles was as the assistant to the director of the Exceptional Children's Foundation, where he concentrated on grant writing. In 1986, the founding president and dean of Charles R. Drew University, M. Alfred Haynes, recruited Paul, asking him to take a finding of the recently issued report by the Secretary of Health and Human Services (HHS), Margaret Heckler, and try to turn it around. Paul chose to address the prevalence of intentional injury cases among minorities, an important factor in the disproportionate health status of minority communities. In choosing to address this area of public health, Paul demonstrated how his experience among the Mayans and the impact of nontraditional academicians in his life had shaped his thinking. With no

precedents to guide him, Paul set out to "make a difference" in Los Angeles just a year after HHS established the Office of Minority Health. The new office advised the Secretary and the Office of Public Health and Science on public health program activities affecting Native Americans, Alaskan Natives, Asian Americans, African-Americans, Hispanics, Native Hawaiians and other Pacific Islanders.

Not only did M. Alfred Haynes give Paul his first opportunity to work on the problem of youth violence and intentional injury, he also became Paul's mentor on population-based approaches to medical care. Dr. Haynes believed that health providers must take responsibility for the population of the community by employing surveillance and other public health techniques to ensure improvements in the health of the entire community. Charles R. Drew Post-Graduate Medical School had been founded in 1966 with state funding in response to the Watts riots. Its mission was to offer post-graduate medical training in the middle of Watts, a medically underserved area of Los Angeles. By the early 1970s a small undergraduate medical education program affiliated with UCLA had been added, with students taking basic science courses at UCLA in the first two years and clinical training at the Los Angeles County Martin Luther King, Jr., Hospital in the last two years.

Paul's work in intentional injuries – e.g., gunshot wounds, stabbings, shattered bones resulting from physical assaults – changed dramatically one weekend, shifting from an academic/research interest to a much more profound personal interest. He had noted an unusually large number of relatives camped out in the corridors of King Hospital that weekend. On Monday morning, when he reviewed the weekend Trauma Log that confirmed 16 homi-

cides already, he came face to face with the families stretching down an entire corridor and around the corner. Anxiously awaiting word from the trauma and intensive care units, they did not yet know whether their sons would survive their injuries. When Paul inquired of a social worker whether the hospital staff was doing anything to help the families, he was told nothing – no grief counseling, no assistance whatsoever for families suffering the stress of not knowing whether their sons would live or die.

The public points its finger at the drug trade and youth gangs as the primary cause of youth violence, a common misperception. While it is true that youth gangs participate in the drug trade across the nation and struggle to protect their turf, most of the victims Paul encountered at King Hospital were not in fact gang members. Ranging in ages from 20 to 34, the victims were typically black or Latino, single, not connected to any social network, transient, and living alone. Somehow they had been caught up in a situation where someone was drinking and things got out of control. Men were far more likely to suffer gunshot wounds, while women were far more likely to suffer nonfatal physical assaults.

Based on that one traumatic weekend at King Hospital, and responding to his mentor's advice to take responsibility for the population of the community by employing surveillance and other public health techniques, Paul co-founded and became an active volunteer in a grief counseling support network, Loved Ones of Homicide Victims (LOHV). His co-founders were Saundrea Young, the social worker he had talked to that sobering Monday morning, and Norma Johnson, a Victim Witness Coordinator with the City of Los Angeles. Paul helped ensure the survival of LOHV by securing grants. Meeting

initially in space donated by the Sunnyside Baptist Church, and helped in attracting clients by the Victims of Crime Act and word of mouth, this much-needed organization soon began contributing vital services to the community.

The grief counseling offered by LOHV became a first step toward a public health approach to youth violence. What had been regarded previously as a simple matter of law enforcement came to be viewed in a public health context, as affecting an entire community. Amid the grief and devastation felt by surviving family members, siblings of murdered victims were at particular risk to repeat the cycle of violence, and LOHV worked with the L.A. Police Department to establish new policies to turn grief away from lethal anger. Thanks to the intervention of LOHV, grief counselors are now available to accompany L.A. police officers to homicide scenes to provide support for surviving family members, hastening the healing process.

In the early 1990s, Paul became more involved with preventive health care. In 1991, Paul and two colleagues, Susan Sorenson of UCLA and Billie Weiss of the Los Angeles County Department of Health Services, co-founded the Violence Prevention Coalition (VPC) of Greater Los Angeles, with Paul becoming chair of the policy committee. Starting with 40 members, today VPC has 900 members representing community-based organizations, law enforcement agencies, educators and health providers. By promoting widespread collaboration, VPC has clearly had an impact on the incidence of youth violence and intentional injury in greater Los Angeles.

Among its achievements, VPC lobbied for legislation enacted in California that requires safety devices on all handguns sold and back-

Leading a discussion group
on community projects.

Meeting one on one with
a graduate student.

Paul at The Pyramid, the university's
basketball facility and local landmark.

ground checks. Lobbying the State Super-
intendent of Public Instruction and the State
Legislature, VPC also helped create in California
a mandated curriculum for grades K-12 that
teaches about violence as a public health issue.
VPC mentors 15 neighborhood coalitions in
greater Los Angeles and established challenge
grants for community-based organizations to
begin youth-centered violence prevention activities. VPC also sponsors awareness events such
as a countywide basketball tournament, "Dance
for Peace" and marches.

For VPC, the brightest outcome of their
work has been dramatic decreases in intentional
injury cases in greater Los Angeles. Homicide
had been among the top three causes of death
among 15- to 24-year-olds, and in the city of
Los Angeles, as high as 40-year-olds. According
to the L.A. Police Department, the city of Los
Angeles saw a 34 percent decline in homicides
from 2000 to 2002, and a 60 percent decline
since 1992. VPC has fostered a paradigm shift
among the disciplines that address youth violence — no longer are public health and law
enforcement professionals stuck at opposite
ends of the spectrum.

In 2002, Paul left Drew University after
16 years to join the residency training program in the Department of Family Medicine
at White Memorial Medical Center in Boyle
Heights, a part of East Los Angeles that is
heavily Latino. His work there involved using
Geographic Information System (GIS) software
to determine which medically underserved
areas (MUAs) could qualify for federal funding
to build community health centers. Working
with two family physician residents and taking
federal criteria into account, Paul identified 31
medically underserved areas in the Los Angeles
metropolitan area and applied for federal desig-

nation for 29 of them. With the MUA designa-
tion, inner-city communities with limited
access to primary care physicians are now able
to secure federal funds to establish federally
qualified health centers. These centers will
ensure the availability of affordable health care
to the growing number of poor and uninsured
residents. They will also help batten down the
health care safety net that has been battered by
a funding crisis in the public health system of
Los Angeles County. Public health clinics have
been forced to close and the funding crisis also
threatens public hospitals.

Paul advises young people thinking of
careers in public health to follow their passion,
find a job they are happy in, and as his mentors
taught him, don't be afraid to take the road
least traveled to find new and effective ways to
advocate for change. He believes that a career in
public health makes you responsible for the
health of an entire community, and this focus
on the health of populations allows for widespread improvements, something one on one
health care cannot typically do. Paul's successes
with Loved Ones of Homicide Victims and the
Violence Prevention Coalition of Greater Los
Angeles demonstrate that a shift in focus can
yield positive results for the health of a community. Preventing youth violence in greater Los
Angeles shifted from being a concern of law
enforcement alone to a problem that public
health techniques could help solve. As the
catalyst behind these changes, Paul Juarez has
created new ways to look at youth violence and
new ways to respond to a public health crisis.

Garland Land, MPH

Missouri

Collecting, organizing and translating data into public health action

Gathering solid, reliable data may not be perceived as a cutting-edge discipline, but it lies at the heart of what the public health community accomplishes on behalf of populations. Data must be collected, organized and translated into action, allowing the public health community to make informed choices about population-based approaches to health interventions. A cancer registry, for example, will tell a state health department and its partners about patterns of disease in the population. Are there clusters? Is there genetic predisposition? Which age groups are most susceptible? Are other patterns revealed and new cases prevented? Only when the public health community gains full access to data, and interprets it from every angle, can health problems be addressed effectively.

Among all U.S. states, Missouri leads the way in collecting, organizing and translating data into action. Why Missouri? Garland Land, director of the Center for Health Information Management

and Evaluation at the Missouri Department of Health and Senior Services since 1971, has earned a reputation as a visionary, always five years ahead of the rest of the nation. He is fortunate that the leadership of Missouri has been accepting of change. Reporting directly to the director of health, he finds that all the directors he has served over the years have supported his initiatives. Reporting to the top, rather than being buried in the organization, gives him the advantage of learning what data are needed to respond to emerging public health issues. In addition, Garland has recruited and trained an excellent staff to which he delegates freely, knowing they will successfully carry out tasks and projects. While Garland has the vision, his staff has the technical expertise and implementation skills. They are devoted to him.

Born and raised in Independence, Missouri, Garland attended William Chrisman High School and then Graceland College in Lamoni, Iowa. Located just over the Missouri border in southwest Iowa, Graceland is a small religious college affiliated with the Community of Christ Church. Garland graduated in three years with a major in mathematics and minor in biology. He headed straight to the University of Michigan School of Public Health to study for his master's degree in public health, drawn by a flier posted at Graceland offering a generous stipend to students interested in biostatistics. Garland qualified for the stipend due to his family's modest finances and his interest in biostatistics study. He received his MPH in 1968. Unlike many others who find themselves drawn to public health after beginning other careers, Garland set his sights on public health from the beginning.

From 1968 until 1971, Garland worked in Kansas City in the "War on Poverty" as a research

director. When he left Ann Arbor, he intended to join the U.S. Public Health Service Corps, and while awaiting word on his application, he volunteered at an anti-poverty program in Independence. When he learned that an old knee injury would keep him out of the Service Corps, he took the research position in Kansas City and began work with the anti-poverty program in earnest. His background in biostatistics proved useful in his research work. Happily, the supervisory experience he gained in Kansas City helped qualify him for the public health position in Jefferson City that followed.

In 1970, while he was still working in the "War on Poverty," Garland married Sarah, a nursing student from Independence who became the supervisor of pediatric and obstetrical nursing at a Jefferson City hospital. They have two grown daughters, both now living in the Kansas City area. Garland's church in Jefferson City has a lay ministry and the congregation elected him pastor several years ago, re-electing him in subsequent years. Garland and Sarah also run an antiques business at the Lake of the Ozarks, renting space to 40 dealers. Beginning as just a hobby years ago, the antiques business has become a passion. During vacations, Garland and Sarah often drive to New England, traveling from town to town buying for their shop and carefully studying the trends.

When Garland joined the Missouri Department of Health and Senior Services in 1971, he supervised a staff of 25. Today, that staff has grown to 220. Then, most staff members were keypunch operators, entering data day in and day out. Today, the staff oversees large information systems, vital records, and health statistics. The state is the central depository of all birth and death records and the records are made accessible

to the public through local public health agencies. While Garland's title has changed little over the years, his responsibilities have changed dramatically. The development of new statistical systems and information technology offers new challenges and opportunities.

The Missouri Department of Health and Senior Services has three main divisions: the Division of Community Health, which handles maternal and child health, chronic disease and nutrition; the Division of Environmental Health and Communicable Diseases; and the Division of Senior Services and Regulation, which handles all regulatory and licensing functions. Garland's unit analyzes birth data, death data, abortions, teen pregnancy and chronic disease data for the Division of Community Health while it creates major surveillance systems for reporting infectious diseases for the Division of Environmental Health and Communicable Diseases. Garland notes that the program managers he works with tell him that he is selling them something they never knew they needed. Garland defines his role as consulting with program managers to determine which health problems need to be addressed and then thinking "out of the box" to provide different solutions.

Garland helped create an integrated information system for Missouri called MOHSAIC, a first-of-its-kind relational database that supports multiple public health programs. MOHSAIC brings together all information on an individual into a single system instead of having disparate program-based applications. Under MOHSAIC, the various divisions and programs have different levels of security clearance. They can obtain data that is appropriate to their security level. The WIC program, for example, can check the database to see if a child is immunized and may discover that the child has a metabolic disorder

uncovered through newborn testing. Garland and Charles Stokes, the deputy director who is now president of the Centers for Disease Control Foundation, began the process of creating the integrated database system in 1993. With $25 million spent on the project to date, the work continues as the department now moves from a client-server environment to one that is Internet-based. With Net-based upgrades possible, refining the system will be smoother and less costly. Garland frequently hosts health officials from other states who come to Jefferson City to admire Missouri's handiwork. Many states are still mired in a political environment that makes bringing people together difficult, especially to create a wholly new model for data collection. In Missouri they see that with perseverance and leadership, obstacles can be overcome.

Garland's vision of translating data into action grew into another unique system in Missouri called MICA, Missouri Information for Community Assessment. Currently 24 separate MICAs track statistics such as births, deaths, a cancer registry, motor vehicle deaths, injuries, hospitalizations and emergency room visits in each of Missouri's 114 counties. A new MICA, called the Priority MICA, highlights each county's unique healthcare challenges and allows each county to establish their own priorities. Users can key in up to 10 weighted criteria for determining priorities. The system captures statistics for 40 "diseases" — any health issue that is preventable, including trauma — and prioritizes the diseases based, for example, upon the number of premature deaths for each disease or minority disparities for each disease. Intrigued by the breadth of the Priority MICA system, especially its ability to help counties set priorities, the CDC is collaborating with Missouri to document its potential on a national scale.

In the early 1990s, the Missouri Department of Health and Senior Services faced the challenge of getting hospitals to report their hospital and emergency room data. The Missouri Hospital Association (MHA) opposed new legislation, fearful that hospital charges and discounted rates would become public knowledge. Although this fear proved unfounded, Garland worked with a "renegade" group of hospitals to support this legal requirement. Since hospital administrators influence legislators in every district (hospitals being large employers), the legislation failed several times. The sponsors, a surgeon in the Senate and a labor leader in the House, did not give up, knowing that good legislation takes time. The senator wanted the Missouri Department of Health and Senior Services to publish consumer guides on quality of care, yet another red flag for the MHA. Garland found he had to be flexible to sell the bill, sitting down to negotiate with the MHA and in the end producing a bill that was a true collaboration. For example, although all data gets reported, the MHA receives it first, edits it and forwards it to the health department. The collaborative process improved the legislation, widening the net to include ambulatory surgical centers.

The hospital reporting legislation finally passed in 1993. The process taught Garland that he should always look for ways to build partnerships, and that his vision can succeed only if people work together in a way that removes fear from the process. The MHA and Garland realized that partnership was the best option after they understood each other's concerns and interests. In recognizing that the department's goal was to serve Missourians and not harm hospitals, the MHA got over its fear.

Garland supervised the publication of a consumer guide on obstetrics, an outgrowth

Garland and his Fiscal Manager, Dan O'Rourke, working the budget numbers.

In the computer room with the Director of the Office of Information Systems, Scott Willett.

Reviewing work assignments with Rena Watts.

With his wife, Sarah, at the antique shop.

Garland meeting with staff members on a new project with (l to r) Mark Van Tuinem, Craig Ward, Kanwal Sandhu, and Jody Clark.

of the legislation and a way to ensure quality of care. The guide reported rates of Caesarean sections and other obstetrics policies in place at each hospital in Missouri. Six months later, Garland's staff returned to the hospitals to see if any changes had been made. They found that hospitals with major competitors made significant improvements. The guide, in fact, became more beneficial to providers than to people choosing hospitals. Other guides followed including one that shows the volume of high-risk procedures performed in hospitals. The guide offers important information to consumers, validating the scientific literature's findings that the more hospitals perform high-risk procedures, the better job they tend to do with them. The guides promote centers of excellence among Missouri's hospitals.

State government cutbacks since 2000 have meant a 40 percent loss in budget revenues for Garland's Center for Health Information Management and Evaluation. One result of the cutbacks is that publication of new consumer guides has been delayed. To make up that critical amount and continue creating new initiatives, Garland courts foundations such as The Robert Wood Johnson Foundation and the Missouri Foundation for Health. He also actively pursues federal grants. A recent grant allowed Missouri to look at statistics for what goes wrong in hospitals, known as medical errors, with a view towards finding ways to reduce them.

The department has district offices throughout the state, but Garland's travels usually take him to meetings out of state. He is principal investigator for several federal grants he and his staff won through competitive bids; these take him frequently to the CDC in Atlanta and to the CDC's National Center for Health Statistics in Hyattsville, Maryland. He also serves on several national committees. Garland finds that his involvement with national projects provides him with the inspiration and ideas to find resources that help create new systems for Missouri. His current projects involve him in studies of newborn hearing surveillance, child maltreatment, very low birth-weight infants, birth defects and motor vehicle injuries.

Garland advises others thinking of careers in public health that the field is a noble calling. He sees the primary purpose of public health as preventing disease or disability. The field is service-oriented and focuses on all people in a community, not just on low-income populations (a common misperception about public health). The field is broad and constantly challenging. In his work, Garland moves from cancer to heart disease to autism to STDs, to name just a few diseases. Those with a bent toward education, statistics, clinical medicine or marketing will find roles in public health. In fact, most types of expertise can play a role in public health, and every day is a new day.

Looking ahead, advances in technology continue to astound Garland and he expects no letup in the pace of dramatic changes in information systems. Ten years ago, he could not have dreamed of the improvements he has seen in medical recordkeeping efficiency, and he believes the same will hold true 10 years from now. He believes that how national health insurance plays out will be a defining force in public health in the years ahead. Just as Medicaid expanded to include children, other programs will adjust to serve people in need more efficiently. Genetic medicine, especially testing of newborns, will push genomics to the forefront. Although the impact of genomics is still being sorted out, Garland foresees as many as 10 times the number of diseases being tested in newborns.

Unlike others who evolve into careers in public health, Garland Land chose his pathway, biostatistics, right from the start and knew from the beginning that his career would be in public health. Armed with his MPH from the University of Michigan and training in biostatistics, he sought a role that would put his skills to use. His work collecting, organizing and translating health data into action has pushed Missouri to the forefront in the nation. Garland's achievements in information systems, vital records and health statistics have earned him the respect and admiration of his colleagues in his home state and of public health professionals across the nation.

Elizabeth Laposata, MD

Rhode Island

Applying the science of pathology to improve public health and safety

A pathologist is trained to know the science of medicine and to understand the human body in all its exquisite detail, but the training does not stop there. Part of the job is also keeping up with advances in firearms, toxicology, trace evidence, forensic anthropology and forensic dentistry, among other nonmedical areas. A post-mortem exam is really a beginning. From that exam, the pathologist reconstructs a life history and recreates the scene and sequence of death. A grieving family relies on the pathologist as the last physician their loved one will ever have. A good pathologist discovers and reveals information about the life lived, often poignant in its detail, and helps the family come to terms with death. Findings from post-mortem exams, when shared through the media, can also affect the behavior of the whole population.

Elizabeth Laposata has been the chief medical examiner for the state of Rhode Island since 1993. In those years, she has dealt with two mass

disasters – the crash of Egypt Air Flight 990 on October 31, 1999, in the Atlantic Ocean 60 miles off the coast of Nantucket, and The Station nightclub fire in Warwick on February 20, 2003, that in the end killed 100 people. That fire in a crowded nightclub devastated a small state where nearly every citizen knew someone affected. Since both scenes were crime scenes, Elizabeth not only supervised a massive effort to identify remains under the most trying circumstances, she also contributed useful information to ongoing criminal investigations.

A native of the Washington, D.C., area, Elizabeth grew up in Arlington, Virginia, as an only child. Her father was raised in Massachusetts and her mother on a farm in Tennessee; both worked in federal jobs, gravitating to Washington after World War II. As a young child, Elizabeth mistook "only child" for "lonely child." She read avidly and remembers growing so excited reading about Anton van Leeuwenhoek's invention of the microscope that her parents gave her a toy version of the instrument. Under the microscope, she discovered a whole new world that she has continued to explore ever since. She always had the mind of a detective, constantly asking why things are the way they are, probing beyond the surface for answers, seeing many layers in most things and trying to explore them all. When she was in sixth grade, Elizabeth insisted that her mother cut open her pet goldfish when he died, and she believes that impulse set her on the career course she has followed since.

Elizabeth attended Washington-Lee High School in Arlington, graduating in 1971. She headed to Bucknell University in Lewisburg, Pennsylvania, where she majored in biology. She graduated cum laude with honors in biology in 1975, having discovered that her interest in the human body had become a consuming focus.

From Bucknell, Elizabeth headed to Georgetown University Medical Center. After her first year, she transferred to the University of Maryland School of Medicine in Baltimore when the financial support she counted on from D.C. ended and she could no longer afford to continue at Georgetown. In Baltimore, Dr. Russell Fisher, a textbook author who worked in the medical examiner's office, introduced her for the first time to pathology. He taught her that pathology serves the public interest – finding out why someone ran off the road, for example, might lead to the discovery of environmental hazards which, when corrected, would benefit the living. With patients, Elizabeth felt squeamish when she caused pain taking blood or performing procedures; pathology saved her from the fear of that feeling.

After graduating from the University of Maryland School of Medicine in 1979, Elizabeth spent two years at Johns Hopkins in Baltimore studying basic anatomic pathology, followed by two years at St. Louis University studying the subspecialty of forensic pathology. After taking her board exams in both anatomic and forensic pathology, she stayed on in St. Louis to do research on the heart and heart disease, one of the leading causes of death. She accepted a post-doctoral fellowship in the Cardiovascular Division at Washington University's Barnes Hospital and studied the effects of alcohol on the heart, specifically how a particular ethanol metabolite affected cell membranes. With Dr. Louis Lange, she published her findings in an article in *Science*, the first study to cite the effects of fatty acid ethyl esters in humans. She also worked part time in the St. Louis medical examiner's office and remembers a series of deaths due to people being outside in the cold. The medical examiner mobilized an education

campaign to warn people not to drink alcohol when outside temperatures were extremely low, to cover their heads, and to be aware of wind chill readings at all times.

From St. Louis, Elizabeth moved to Philadelphia to do one more year of research on the effects of alcohol on the heart at the University of Pennsylvania Hospital. She also began part time work as an associate medical examiner for the city of Philadelphia, converting to full time work when her post-doctoral fellowship at Penn ended. In 1991, she joined the State of Delaware as a full time associate medical examiner. Her focus on forensics in Delaware brought her to Rhode Island's attention when the Department of Health there sought to fill the position of chief medical examiner.

When Egypt Air Flight 990 crashed in the Atlantic Ocean en route from New York to Cairo in 1999, killing 217 people, the Federal Aviation Administration (FAA) designated Rhode Island as the coordinating site for the Mass Disaster Death Investigation. In her role as chief medical examiner for Rhode Island, Elizabeth Laposata became the head of the investigation. She supervised the installation of mobile temporary mortuaries provided by the federal government, called Disaster Mortuary Operational Response Teams (DMORTs), at the Quonset Point Naval Station on Narragansett Bay. Assisting the FAA in the investigation were the FBI and Coast Guard, who oversaw the collection of human remains and debris at the site of the crash 60 miles out at sea. The Bureau of Alcohol, Tobacco and Firearms and the National Transportation Safety Board were also involved. Everything collected was transported on large vessels back to Quonset Point, with human remains going to Elizabeth's mortuaries for identification and debris to a large hangar for reconstruction.

As is usual in such cases, volunteers arrived from other states to assist Elizabeth and her Rhode Island staff in the work of identifying 5,000 fragmented human remains. Elizabeth's staff had to keep up with their customary day-to-day work all through the disaster, working 12-hour shifts seven days a week through February. The task of identifying thousands of remains represented eight years of normal casework for the Rhode Island medical examiner's office. Within several weeks of the crash, it became apparent that no intact human remains would be recovered. Elizabeth made the decision to concentrate exclusively on DNA analysis, performed at the Armed Forces Institute of Pathology DNA Identification Laboratory in Rockville, Maryland. In the end, nearly two years after the crash, the 217 separate human lives that had been aboard Egypt Air 990 were identified in this way. Fortunately, the families made available direct samples of hair follicles and tissue cells from the hairbrushes and toothbrushes of many victims, easing identification. Also helpful, if medical records indicated operations, were tissue samples from hospital and doctor visits for some victims. For victims who could not be identified with the help of direct samples, Elizabeth and her team constructed extensive family trees and took saliva swabs and blood samples from the nearest living relatives, comparing the DNA to the fragmented remains.

Elizabeth met personally each afternoon with the relatives who had flown from their homes in Egypt, the Sudan, France and elsewhere to Rhode Island to be near the disaster scene. She traveled to the hotel in Newport where they were staying and described to them in plain language each day's progress, answered questions as informatively as possible, and provided support to grieving family members at a horrific time in their lives. Even when no definitive information could be shared,

the ritual of the briefing became a touchstone for the families each day, bringing them together in shared grief and showing them that the tasks and obligations of daily life continued. One of Elizabeth's greatest challenges was relating why the remains recovered from the ocean floor at the crash site were not intact. In explaining how the human body's tensile strength could not withstand the crash into water, she in effect gave the families the cause of death – extreme body fragmentation due to massive blunt force trauma.

Elizabeth faced other challenges – returning personal effects to the grieving families in a way that preserved evidence and reconstructing injury patterns whenever possible from the fragmented remains. These reconstructions assisted the FBI and FAA in determining just how the plane crashed. In retrospect, the disaster can be seen as a precursor to the September 2001 terrorist attacks on the World Trade Center and Pentagon. Investigators found no mechanical failure and concluded that the pilot appeared to willfully fly the plane into the ocean.

On February 20, 2003, Elizabeth was awakened around midnight by an associate at the medical examiner's office warning her of the potential for another mass disaster. Pyrotechnics during a band's performance had ignited the stage of The Station, a packed nightclub in Warwick, and the fire spread quickly throughout the building. It became clear immediately that the fire, which caused patrons to stampede toward one working exit, would take scores of lives. In the early morning hours, Elizabeth mobilized her mortuary in Providence. Medical vans began transporting victims there almost immediately and a nonstop frenzy of activity ensued for days afterward. DMORT arrived to assist the Rhode Island staff, stretched thin once again. Elizabeth reviewed the findings of staff to confirm positive

With anthropology student Angel Desmarais, examining identifying characteristics of bone.

In the examination room, recording preliminary facts with M.E. agent Lynne DeStephano.

Checking in with front office staff Jessica Gervais.

Morning meeting in the medical examiner's office.

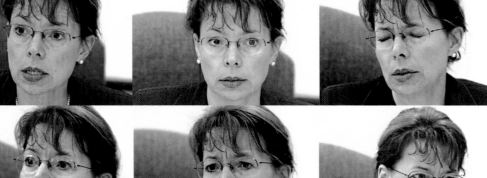

With "woman's best friend" Etta, her Siberian Husky.

Doing research at Sarah Doyle Women's Center at Brown University.

Troubleshooting a report with senior scene investigator Scott Mowry.

identification and relayed information through the Family Assistance Center to families who were waiting to hear the fate of their loved ones. Along with the families, all Rhode Islanders mourned the senseless loss of loved ones, neighbors and friends. Dental charts proved to be the best means for quickly identifying remains. Causes of death ranged from smoke inhalation to suffocation to burns and were determined by a combination of examination of the body and testing of body fluids. Each death cataloged by the medical examiner's office – 96 bodies recovered at the scene, nearly all not recognizable, and four who died later in hospitals from severe burns – will be key evidence in the criminal trials that await the owners of the nightclub. As a result of the findings, the Rhode Island Legislature enacted new public health protections, fire safety regulations and inspection regimens.

Elizabeth's advice to people thinking of careers in public health is to be exposed to many things. When you find something you like, as she did in pathology, go after it. She cautions that well-meaning people may take you off course. As for pathology, it allows you to be both a medical detective and a grief counselor. The families of murder victims sometimes wait years before they consult Elizabeth about the last moments of life for their loved ones. She sits with these families to answer their questions as honestly as she can and helps bring closure to at least part of their pain. She finds their courage moving. As the public health community recognizes more and more that violence is a public health issue, the work of the medical examiner will grow even more prominent.

Pathologists are key to identifying preventable causes of death and thereby play a key role in protecting the public's health. Two types of pathology coexist: forensic pathology and hospital pathology. Following a hospital death, if the family permits an autopsy, hospital-based pathologists determine clinical and pathological correlations. An autopsy is not required in all cases, as significant medical history may be available to answer questions as they arise. In the field of forensic pathology, the medical examiner must by law determine the cause of death in cases of suspected foul play, e.g., homicide, suicide or accident or if the cause of death is unknown. By learning causes and the manner of death, the medical examiner plays a role in informing the community about preventable and accidental causes of death. Often, an autopsy relieves pressure by not finding a public health impact. In both instances, unresolved grief can be debilitating, so the pathologist seeks to put to rest the aspect of not knowing how and why a loved one died.

Looking ahead, Elizabeth believes public health will be better-funded, allowing for increased investment in resources. While prevention is usually not taken seriously until something bad happens, the population seems to be growing better-informed. Increasingly, people question treatment options and medication choices and seek data prior to making important health care decisions. In Rhode Island, people use the medical examiner's office to obtain mortality statistics for certain surgical procedures such as gastric bypass operations. Here, the medical examiner's office provides important data to the public to aid in their decision-making.

Public health is fortunate to have pathology as an active partner. As Elizabeth Laposata points out, the post-mortem exam really is the beginning. The exam reconstructs a life now ended to benefit the living. While much of the work of the medical examiner relates to the individual, findings of fact will influence behavior in the whole population. In this way, pathology serves a vital role in public health.

Marci Layton, MD

New York

Investigating New York's first West Nile virus outbreak

A mysterious virus appeared in the borough of Queens in New York City in 1999 and quickly developed into an outbreak. The story of how the virus was identified and contained offers a real-life example of how public health methods – and a little luck – can halt the spread of disease. As the lead epidemiologist in the case, Marcelle Layton, MD led her team from the New York City Department of Health (NYCDOH) in a classic public health response to a disease outbreak.

The team began investigating the mysterious outbreak as soon as the first two cases were reported by one astute infectious disease physician from a small hospital in Northern Queens. The culprit, the West Nile virus, had never been seen before in the Western hemisphere, and the clinical presentation was nonspecific and difficult to distinguish from other viral encephalitis diseases. Ruling nothing out, but well before identifying the actual viral cause and its source, Marci's team began an active epidemiological investigation and also began to develop contingency plans based on potential worst-case scenarios. They began taking detailed histories from the relatives, friends and neighbors of the initial patients, notified the medical community by sending a broadcast fax and e-mail Health Alert and started to actively survey all hospitals in the city to identify additional cases.

Within two days, they had uncovered eight patients with the same mysterious constellation of symptoms reported by the Queens physician. Given that these patients were all older adults,

none of their close contacts reported being ill, and they had no common exposures besides spending time outdoors in the evening hours, the team believed that the most likely cause was an arbovirus carried by mosquitoes. Therefore, even before the CDC reported the initial laboratory results, Marci and her colleagues at the NYCDOH, as well as the Mayor's Office of Emergency Management, began planning for a campaign of active mosquito control to prevent a more serious outbreak in New York City.

Marci Layton has been an assistant commissioner of the NYCDOH in the Bureau of Communicable Disease since 1994. She came to New York City in 1992, assigned as an Epidemic Intelligence Service (EIS) officer by the Centers for Disease Control and Prevention (CDC) in Atlanta. When her two-year fellowship ended, her supervisor in New York City was just retiring. She was offered his position and decided to continue working at the NYCDOH.

A native of Baltimore, Maryland, Marci is the eldest of three children. Her younger brother and sister are twins. Her father worked in real estate, and her mother was a homemaker and a secretary. Marci attended the University of Maryland in College Park and majored in microbiology, a choice that played to her academic strength in the sciences. As a high school and college student, she had worked as a volunteer at both an emergency department in a children's hospital and at St. Elizabeth's Hospital for the mentally ill in Washington, D.C., as well as at summer programs for physically and mentally handicapped children and adults in Pennsylvania and Vermont, and these experiences helped her determine she wanted to be a physician. As a college student, she developed an interest in immunology working in a campus research laboratory developing monoclonal antibodies.

After graduating from the University of Maryland, Marci attended one year of medical school at the University of Pennsylvania in Philadelphia before transferring to Duke University in Durham, North Carolina. She initially wanted to be a primary care physician, a noted strength of the Duke program but an area she realized the University of Pennsylvania did not emphasize at the time. Duke also encouraged study away from campus and in 1983 Marci took most of one year away, arranging three very different internships that gave her valuable perspective on healthcare delivery systems and cross-cultural medicine. She traveled to Chiang Mai, Thailand, where she worked in a small hospital with a missionary physician. She worked for the Indian Health Service in Gallup, New Mexico, with Bruce Tempest, who later identified the first patients infected with Hanta virus during the 1993 outbreak of unexpected deaths among Native Americans. She also worked with primary care physicians and their patients in Appalachia in the border area where Virginia, North Carolina and Tennessee meet.

Marci was torn between internal medicine and family practice for her residency program. Realizing she preferred working with older adults, she chose internal medicine and moved to Syracuse, New York, and the Upstate Medical Center of the State University of New York (SUNY Upstate) for her residency. A happy result of living in Syracuse was the chance for Marci to get to know the Adirondack Mountains where she frequently went hiking (and still does) during her time off.

Rather than pursue a fellowship after her residency, Marci worked in a medically underserved area. She joined the Providence Ambulatory Health Care Foundation in Rhode Island for a year and a half and provided primary care medicine to a diverse population, including Hmong refugees, a large Hispanic population from many different Central American countries and Cape Verdeans, among others. Looking for new intellectual challenges, Marci applied for an Infectious Disease fellowship at Yale University and was accepted. Before moving to New Haven, Connecticut, to begin her new position, she again took time to travel, this time to Katmandu, Nepal, to volunteer in a clinic for three months. Unlike the small hospital in Chiang Mai, which had been a beautiful facility, she worked in true third-world conditions in Nepal.

Completing her fellowship in 1992, Marci signed up for a two-year commitment as an EIS officer with the CDC, where she was assigned to the NYCDOH. Her class included 85 fellow officers. Before starting the program in Atlanta she once again traveled, this time to Barrow, Alaska, where she substituted for a physician for six weeks and practiced primary care medicine for the last time – from delivering babies to treating patients after a polar bear attack.

The EIS experience immersed Marci in epidemiology. Her success in this field prompted the CDC to honor her in 2002 by inviting her to deliver the Alexander Langmuir Lecture, an annual lecture during the EIS conference honoring the founder of the EIS program. She addressed the topic of public health and terrorism, pointing out the key lessons learned during the anthrax outbreak in 2001. These included the challenges in making acute decisions before data was fully available to understand the outbreak and that the epidemiology and clinical aspects of naturally occurring anthrax did not apply to incidents of weapons grade anthrax released in indoor settings. The lessons also included the value of partnering with law enforcement when responding to bioterrorism, the need to proactively respond to the mental health impact of terrorism and, not least, that effective communication (to the medical community, the public and public health partners worldwide) underlies every aspect of a successful response.

During the 10 years Marci has been with the Bureau of Communicable Disease of the NYCDOH, her program has investigated many new infectious disease threats in New York City. Separate bureaus deal with tuberculosis and sexually transmitted diseases, including HIV/AIDS, while the Bureau of Communicable Disease deals with all the others. Marci views it as the "firehouse" of the NYCDOH, responding instantly to any emergency with, in effect, all sirens blaring.

In late August 1999, a call came into the bureau from a Queens physician, Dr. Deborah Asnis, who was treating two patients at Flushing Hospital for what appeared to be either botulism or viral encephalitis. One patient had muscle weakness to the point of paralysis. Marci did not think the cause was botulism based on the clinical and laboratory findings, but she sent investigators from the NYCDOH to Flushing Hospital to review the patients' charts and draw specimens that were sent for analysis first to the Wadsworth Laboratory in Albany, part of the New York State Department of Health.

Within a week, two additional encephalitis cases were reported, one at this same hospital and a second by a neurologist familiar with the Flushing Hospital cases who had just seen a fourth patient with encephalitis with muscle weakness in a nearby hospital in Queens. These two cases were reported to Marci late on a Friday afternoon, prompting her and a colleague, Dr. Annie Fine, to drive to Flushing themselves to investigate. The four patients, all older adults, lived in the Whitestone section of Queens. All had very similar clinical presentations; of most

DEPT OF HEALTH & MENTAL HYGIENE
BUREAU OF TUBERCULOSIS CONTROL   216
SONAL MUNSIFF MD   DIRECTOR
MARIE DORSINVILLE RN MPH PMO
MARY MASTERSON DIR OF OPERATIONS   219
FABIENNE LARAQUE MD MPH DIR OF SURVEILLANCE

COMMUNICABLE DISEASE PROGRAM   225
MARCI LAYTON MD ASST COMMISSIONER   222

concern was severe muscle paralysis requiring all four to be put on ventilators to support their respiratory muscles. None were well enough to be interviewed so Marci and her colleague relied on family members and neighbors to reconstruct their recent histories.

Realizing that only two general types of viral encephalitis tend to cause outbreaks in the late summer, Marci and her team first ruled out an enterovirus (e.g., intestinal virus) which often occurs sporadically in New York City at this time of year, and then began to concentrate on an arbovirus (e.g., mosquito-borne) as the source. As the NYCDOH no longer had a vector control program, the bureau turned to the American Museum of Natural History to lend an entomologist to the investigation. Based on interviews of the family members of the patients, Marci's team learned that all had spent time outdoors during the two weeks before their illness, in their gardens or in the neighborhood, in areas that had plenty of sources of standing water – an excavated pool site, old tires, rain barrels. At the time, New York City had been suffering from a drought that prompted one of the cases, a gardener, to collect rainwater to keep his garden green and growing. This patient, the first fatality of the 1999 outbreak, had spent many early mornings sleeping outside on a lounge chair near one of his rain barrels. When the entomologist and the team from the NYCDOH visited his home, this rain barrel was filled with mosquito larvae.

The team was convinced it was dealing with a mosquito-borne virus, most probably St. Louis encephalitis virus, since this virus has been seen in the area in the past. With the contingency plans already in place, New York City was able to start insecticide spraying within hours of the CDC reporting the initial results that antibody tests from the patients had tested positive for St. Louis encephalitis (as it turns out, a very close cousin of West Nile virus). It wasn't until a month later that the CDC recognized that the actual cause of the outbreak was West Nile virus, based on avian specimens obtained from a separate investigation of deaths among birds in the city. Fortunately, the control measures for St. Louis encephalitis and West Nile virus are the same.

A lesson of the West Nile outbreak – the need for better coordination between public health authorities and veterinarians and the wildlife community – came at a painful cost. Marci only discovered four weeks after the human cases first presented that veterinarians and wildlife biologists at the Bronx Zoo and the New York State Department of Environmental Conservation had been investigating an increased number of deaths among crows, that in retrospect began turning up in the area in June. However, the cause of these deaths took months to determine, and it was not until the media publicized the human outbreak that specimens were tested appropriately for viral causes, leading to the identification of West Nile virus in late September.

No one knows how the West Nile virus was introduced to the United States. Likely borne by birds, either through importation or by a freak migratory route, the virus introduction led to widespread avian deaths because North American birds were not resistant. The virus becomes more concentrated in the blood of birds than humans, and crows are more susceptible than other birds for reasons not yet fully known.

The 1999 outbreak in the New York City area caused 62 cases and seven deaths. The next year the NYCDOH laboratory acquired the capacity to test for the virus, as did most public health labs across the country. The department also developed a comprehensive mosquito control program to prevent a recurrence. Since 1999, the number of West Nile cases in New York City has remained relatively low; the virus spread quickly throughout the country, however, with 2003 the worst year since 1999 (over 8,900 cases). With the knowledge that the virus is now endemic in the United States, communities must take countermeasures each year, eliminating standing water and larviciding areas such as storm drains and sewage treatment plants. Insecticide spraying is used only as a last resort if virus levels in the mosquito population become high enough to cause a potential human outbreak.

Although much concern has been raised about the health effects of spraying, less attention has been paid to the long-term consequences of the disease itself. Among the survivors of the 1999 outbreak in Queens, many were severely debilitated and never returned to their normal level of activity. One positive outcome, however, is that the NYCDOH made improving linkages with the animal health community a priority, and now, similar to human disease, many animal diseases are legally reportable.

Marci's priority since joining the Bureau of Communicable Diseases in 1994 has been improving communication with health care providers, including the first broadcast fax and e-mail health alert system in the United States, to facilitate rapid notification regarding acute public health issues. The experience with the West Nile virus outbreak led to a veterinary alert system as well. Through a secure Web site that replaced the original notification method, the system sends out information quickly to the health care provider community on issues ranging from SARS to monkeypox. As important as communication with providers is to Marci, ensuring that her staff is always ready and receptive when a physician calls is equally important, as one never knows when the next West Nile virus-like outbreak may be reported.

With Dr. Vern Bethea.

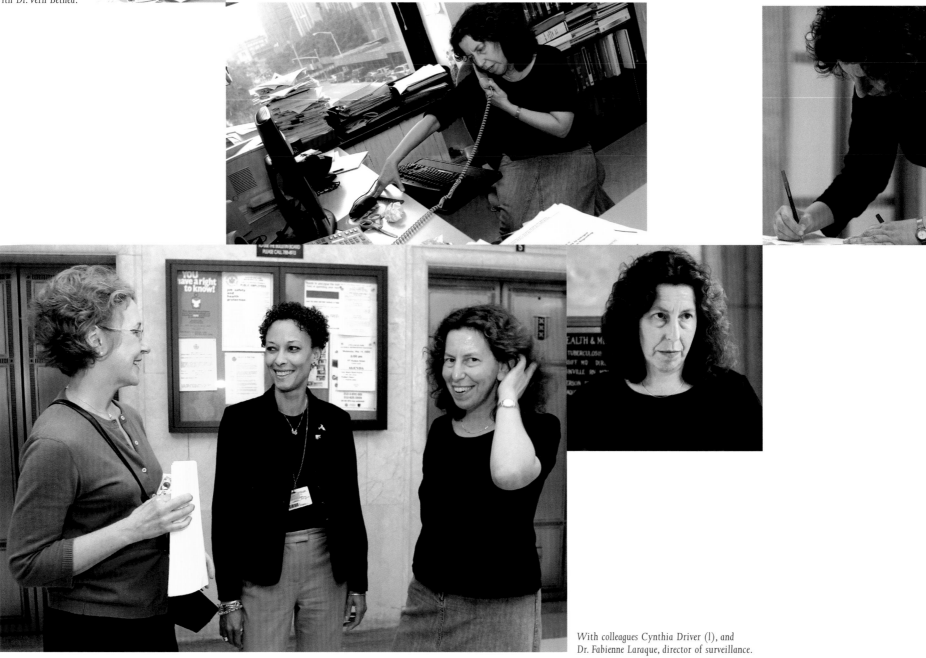

With colleagues Cynthia Driver (l), and
Dr. Fabienne Laraque, director of surveillance.

In 10 years, Marci's staff has grown to 70 from 15 and to eight physicians from one. Statisticians and an epidemiologist run a syndromic surveillance system, which started by collecting statistics on 911 ambulance calls. It expanded in stages to include emergency department visits, then pharmacy sales and finally to tracking absenteeism in a large city agency. The system allows Marci and her staff to identify patterns of illness that may represent an outbreak and to expedite investigations to determine the cause. The bureau also focuses on prevention through health education, and recent federal funding has allowed Marci to hire a public health educator to develop community campaigns to address disease issues of current concern.

Some of the challenges Marci and her staff continue to face are antibiotic resistance, viral hepatitis, and most recently the threat of imported diseases such as SARS. As a crossroads for large numbers of world travelers, New York City must always stay alert for unexpected diseases. During the worldwide SARS outbreak in 2003, the bureau received reports of over 300 suspected cases, although only 27 met the CDC clinical and epidemiologic criteria and none were confirmed to be SARS based on laboratory testing. Isolation of patients, and if indicated quarantine of their contacts, are essential tools for dealing with SARS and prompted Marci and her staff to re-evaluate and improve the department's legal and operational plans for managing a highly contagious outbreak.

Having found her way to public health from medicine, Marci enjoys a field that is very diverse. With New York City's melting pot population, the challenges are never ending. No day is the same, and new twists become the expected. In her government work, Marci relies on the health care community, academics, emergency management officials and law enforcement as partners and works hard to build bridges to those communities. She enjoys her work with nonphysicians and the many populations of New York City and never grows bored. The attraction of a public health career for her is first and foremost the ability to make a difference.

Looking ahead, Marci sees a growing recognition and appreciation of public health among the general public. The federal government's infusion of funding since 1999 and especially since September 11, 2001, has helped. Funding streams can change very rapidly in government, however, and Marci believes the public health community must promote its accomplishments – when public health works well, its results are usually invisible to the public. From an infectious disease standpoint, further enhancements in staff capacity, information technology and communication infrastructure are still needed to confront new and emerging disease threats, including bioterrorism. Especially troubling would be an intentional disease outbreak, such as one caused by smallpox or a natural outbreak due to a highly contagious disease, such as pandemic influenza. Fortunately, the public health infrastructure needed to respond to either intentional or natural outbreaks is the same. As with any public service career, public health depends for its success on attracting and retaining qualified staff – in this case, with expertise in surveillance, epidemiology, statistics, medicine, information technology and health education.

New Yorkers owe much to Marci Layton's gifts in epidemiology. The 1999 West Nile outbreak could have been far more devastating if not for the swift and sure work of Marci and the staff at the NYCDOH. As with many in the public health community, they are unsung heroes.

Randy Lee, RN

Arkansas

Putting "Children First" in his community

The families of Miller County, Arkansas, are fortunate to have Randy Lee in their midst. A nurse by training and a public health professional by choice, Randy touches the lives of families by putting children first. Among many accomplishments in his public health career, Randy is proudest of the Our Children First (OCF) coalition he built in Miller County. An example of public health leadership, the coalition shows how public health can become part of the very fabric of a community, a provider of primary care where none existed.

Although not an Arkansas native, Randy grew up in East Texas, just 75 miles south of the Arkansas border. His father was a chemist at ICI, a manufacturer of carbon products and the largest employer in Marshall, Randy's hometown. As he grew up, Randy knew he wanted to work in health care, influenced in part by his mother's death when he was nine years old.

After graduating from high school in 1972, Randy headed to Texas A&M University to major in zoology, a step toward a medical career. Midway through, conscious of fiercely competitive standards for admission to medical school, Randy changed his mind. He transferred to the University of Texas at El Paso to study nursing. Randy's high school sweetheart, who had transferred from Baylor University to Texas A&M to be with him, supported him through the nursing program by teaching kindergarten in El Paso.

They married in 1976. Randy's wife still teaches kindergarten, and they have two grown sons.

In 1978, Randy graduated with a Bachelor of Science in nursing degree. Male nurses were rare in those days, and although Randy knew he would be able to find a job easily, he did not want to work in a hospital setting. Fortunately for the people of Arkansas, Randy's cousin – a communicable disease nurse with the Arkansas Department of Health – lured him from Texas to Arkansas. She persuaded him that the Arkansas public health system was small enough for him to make a tangible impact. His first job was as a public health nurse intern in the Miller County Health Unit in Texarkana. Even though Randy began his career in public health on the lowest rung of the ladder, he was hooked.

Over the years, Randy rose through the ranks of the Arkansas Department of Health. From 1982 to 2000, he served as area manager for the eight counties surrounding Texarkana. When the State Department of Health reorganized in 2000 into five regions, he became regional director for Southwest Arkansas, responsible for 17 counties. Thanks to a nomination by Dr. Joycelyn Elders when she was State Health Director, the Kellogg Foundation awarded Randy a three-year fellowship, which paid for a quarter of his time and allowed him to travel extensively across the country to study leadership models. Such fellowships provide public health professionals like Randy with invaluable opportunities for growth in their chosen field, enhancing their vision of what can be done in their own communities.

Unlike many other states, the Arkansas Department of Health provides primary care services to a large percentage of the state's population. Medicaid waivers allow the Arkansas Department of Health to serve people on a sliding scale above the poverty line, generally up to 200

percent. Services include family planning and maternal and child health. Department employees, all of whom are state workers, deal with sexually transmitted diseases, chronic diseases, tuberculosis, HIV/AIDS, in-home services, and many other primary care services.

In 1993, in Texarkana and Miller Counties, a staggering 25 percent of the children lived below the poverty line. The rate of teenage pregnancy led the state. Families and providers alike found the social services delivery system to be fragmented and difficult to navigate. Low-income families could rarely find medical and dental care providers for their children, and when they needed providers, they usually ended up in hospital emergency rooms. Social services for these children simply did not exist. Randy set out to remedy the situation.

Assisted by community activists committed to overcoming disparities in health care, Randy brought together the state health and human services departments in a coalition with ARKids, the state's Children's Health Insurance Program (CHIP). He then spearheaded an application to the Robert Wood Johnson (RWJ) Foundation to secure a Child Health Initiative Grant, specifically targeting low-income children in Miller County. With careful shepherding, the coalition made the three-year, $1.5 million grant last nearly five years. The grant required that the county's health coalition provide case management services to a specific group of high-risk children, publish a child health report card annually, and develop flexible funding streams beyond direct state appropriations.

Randy became the administrator and program director for the Child Health Initiative Grant. He met his first great challenge – to find the right person to shepherd the grant – by hiring Debbie Lashford as program manager. He knew Debbie through her volunteer work with the Junior

League. She had helped him set up a dental clinic and had campaigned with him for community water fluoridation.

Randy, Debbie and a small staff involved the community in addressing health care disparities among low-income children. Before long, they decided the community should drive the program, not the coalition of state agencies. They spun it off as a 501(c)(3) nonprofit community coalition and renamed the program the Our Children First (OCF) coalition. Debbie became executive director. Eight years later, Randy still sits on the executive committee and continues to work closely with Debbie. Their successes have allowed OCF to expand from Miller County into nearby counties.

The top priority of OCF is parenting education. More than 450 parents have participated in OCF parenting workshops, which run in 10-week blocks and involve, on average, from 12 to 15 parents. In a typical session, about half of the parents attend by court order, the other half by referrals. The courses have succeeded with both types of parents and prevent entry (or re-entry) of children into state child protective services.

The next priority of OCF is prevention of teenage pregnancy. Over a three-year period, OCF ran an extensive abstinence campaign through the media and at the same time, worked in several school districts with teenage students, teaching them to make responsible choices about dating and sex. OCF also secured grants from the State Health Department to provide family planning outreach and education. In the past year alone, the family planning units have seen more than 1,000 patients. The teen pregnancy rate fell from 22.2 percent in 1994 to 17 percent in 1999, and births to girls aged 17 and under decreased from 9 percent in 1994 to 5.7 percent in 1999.

Another important priority for OCF was securing Medicaid coverage for children and pregnant women. By publicizing the lack of providers at the local and state levels, OCF helped hundreds of children and families acquire both Medicaid coverage and primary care physicians. OCF played a vital role in linking uninsured children to the ARKids program, and since 1998 has lessened the shortage of coverage dramatically. In 2002, enrollment in ARKids in the eight counties served by OCF increased by more than 3,000 children.

Among other accomplishments, OCF advocated for public transportation, chartered Transitional Employment Assistance for Miller County, and improved the flow and format of educational information. OCF continues to host an annual "Wild About Wellness" event. OCF also funds the good decision-making curriculum in the schools, helps people negotiate the system to secure appropriate health care and social services, and perhaps most importantly, weaves stories out of statistics, the surest way to gain people's backing for needed public health initiatives.

In the past five years, communities throughout Arkansas have conducted annual surveys of youth risk behavior. The findings, tabulated in report cards, focus on the use of drugs and alcohol, sex, pregnancy, STDs and violence among youth and are usually an eye-opener for the community. The State Department of Health facilitates discussions about what can be done, and helps communities form Hometown Health Improvement coalitions in response. Randy's contributions to the planning process have been key to getting the Hometown Health Improvement coalitions up and running, a perfect example of Randy's belief in mobilizing communities to confront their own health care issues.

Randy Lee in the Clark County Health Unit in Arkadelphia, Ark., with Julie Evans awaiting immunization.

Hiking in Big Bend
National Park.

On Caddo Lake (TX) with family:
(l to r) daughter-in-law Heather Lee,
wife Barbara, father-in-law John
Kerr, son Josh, and mother-in-law
Anne. Other family members include
Rudy the golden retriever, and Peaches
the beagle.

Meeting with staff from the
Arkansas Department of Health
(southwest region).

The Hometown Health Improvement coalitions follow the OCF model. The Arkansas State Department of Health assigns team leaders – mostly public health nurses – who in turn tap specialists, trained as facilitators, to work with groups to begin modifying behavior. Once the Hometown Health Improvement coalitions are functioning fully across the state, Arkansas can more successfully tackle unhealthy behaviors and build people's appreciation of public health.

Randy observes that today's problems with obesity, smoking and physical activity are the "clean water" problem of yesterday. He believes these problems can only be tackled successfully if communities work together. Schools need to provide healthy snacks and schedule physical education. Towns need to build sidewalks and parks. Everyone needs to encourage physical activity (Randy himself still coaches youth basketball and baseball). Young people who enter the field of public health will have the opportunity to tackle these problems and make a difference. Key to their training will be learning how to change behavior, with a focus on prevention and cessation.

Ten years from now, Randy sees Arkansas shifting its emphasis away from providing primary care services. Public health professionals will be more involved in facilitating community discussions about obesity, smoking, physical activity and other pressing health issues. Once confronted with the facts, communities will challenge themselves to do something about them.

In the near future, communities in Arkansas will need to mobilize, one by one, if unhealthy lifestyle choices are to be modified. Thanks to Randy Lee's vision of community ownership of public health, first shaped with OCF in Miller County, one community's success story will soon spread throughout Arkansas, and possibly across the country.

Aggie Leitheiser, RN, MPH

Minnesota

Bridging agencies to focus on
emergency preparedness

"Be prepared," best known as the Boy Scouts motto, has always equally applied to public health. In the aftermath of September 11, 2001, and subsequent anthrax incidents, preparedness became a pressing public policy issue and a national buzzword. Minnesota, like all states across the country, received special federal funding to rethink its approach to public health preparedness. The funding called for the existing public health infrastructure to work with the FBI, National Guard, fire departments, police departments, the attorney general's office, local agencies, hospitals, clinics, laboratories and health care providers to coordinate a first response to biological or chemical terrorism. In Minnesota, leadership for this challenging task fell to Aggie Leitheiser, a longtime staff member of the state's Department of Health. Aggie's diverse public health career made her the perfect choice to head Minnesota's preparedness activities.

Like each state in the union, Minnesota has its own personality and civic culture. Minnesotans by their nature love to attend meetings and are active and willing participants in public forums and volunteer activities. Aggie knew from experience to involve as many Minnesotans as possible in the integration process and to be inclusive in the decision-making process. Rather than viewing the key players as separate entities, Aggie recognized that health professionals working together as partners could accomplish health

protection. She also emphasized considering the far-reaching health consequences of decisions on both public health and health care systems.

Aggie's ability to interact successfully with many people and situations comes in part from her upbringing. Born in South Dakota in the little town of Emery, 50 miles west of Sioux Falls, Aggie grew up on a 250-acre farm with seven siblings. The farm grew corn and oats, raised pigs and chickens and ran a dairy operation with Holstein cows. The seasonal imperatives of farming made Aggie aware of the need for teamwork in meeting daily challenges. "Be prepared" is also the watchword of farmers, never safe from the vagaries of unpredictable weather, unexpected crop failures, fluctuating prices, injuries and illness. Two of Aggie's brothers chose to continue the farming life in South Dakota, one on the family farm, one on an adjoining farm. Fortunately for Minnesota, Aggie chose a different path.

Aggie graduated in 1968 as one of 36 classmates from the local high school, famous for its basketball team. She took the advice of her elder sister, a nurse, and attended South Dakota State University (SDSU) in Brookings to major in nursing. As part of her training, she worked for nine months during her senior year at St. Luke's Hospital in St. Paul, Minnesota. She earned a bachelor's degree in nursing (BSN) in 1972 and after graduation took the boards to become a registered nurse. For her first position, she headed back to St. Luke's Hospital, lured by a small signing bonus and the attraction of the Twin Cities.

Aggie's first nursing job at St. Luke's was in extended care, which she found to be great training for public health. After a year and a half, she switched to the orthopedic floor. Two years later, she moved to Wausau, Wisconsin, to live with several close friends and began work at the

Marathon County Health Department, her first job in public health. The job entailed working in many different disciplines: school nursing, home care, maternal and child health, mental health and community involvement.

After two years learning the basics of public health in Wausau, Aggie moved back to Minneapolis/St. Paul. She became the senior public health nurse at the Wright County Human Services Agency in Buffalo, a suburb west of Minneapolis. Within two weeks of joining the agency, she was asked to write a grant proposal to submit to the Minnesota Department of Health for support of community-based public health. She secured $80,000 to hire public health nurses and health educators and to plan for an expanded public health program for Wright County. Twelve years later, when Aggie left the department, the annual budget had grown to $800,000. Services had expanded to reach a population that had grown to 88,000 from 65,000. Aggie was promoted to the position of Community Health Services supervisor and helped secure and dispense Medicaid and Medicare funds, among many responsibilities.

Aggie's work in Wright County harkened back to her training at South Dakota State University. In her senior year, she had worked with a team of fellow nursing students on a simulation to create a county health department in a county where none had existed. That project guided her in expanding Wright County's public health services to match the county's population growth during her years there. She also represented the State Public Health Nursing Directors Association on the Commissioner's AIDS Task Force.

Beginning in 1981 while working in Wright County, Aggie studied part time at the University of Minnesota for her master's degree in public

health, concentrating on public health administration. She completed the MPH degree eight years later, in 1989, having joined the Minnesota Department of Health in 1988. After completing the degree, Aggie married Jeff Schlosser. Together they have invested in condemned properties in Minneapolis, bringing them up to code and improving the neighborhood.

In 1988, Aggie applied to become Program Advisor for HIV/AIDS at the Minnesota Department of Health and was hired for the job. She moved from being a generalist in Wright County to becoming a specialist for the state of Minnesota. At the time, 300 people had been diagnosed with AIDS in Minnesota, enough to make the public anxious about the state's policies. Her challenge was to make those policies work for HIV/AIDS patients and at the same time alleviate the general public's disquiet about a frightening contagious disease.

Aggie's rise through the Minnesota Department of Health has been steady. After two years in HIV/AIDS, she became a section manager for AIDS and STDs, and two years later assistant division director for Disease Prevention and Control. In addition to HIV/AIDS and STDs, her areas of responsibility have included immunization and chronic and infectious disease epidemiology.

In 1995, the Minnesota Department of Health appointed Aggie division director of Disease Prevention and Control after a national search. Her supervisors recognized that the best candidate for the position was already part of the team. Four years later, she became assistant commissioner. Aggie has been in her current position with the Health Protection Bureau since 1999 and even served as acting commissioner in 2003 during the transition to the current commissioner, Dianne Mandernach.

September 11, 2001, changed the public health landscape throughout the nation and Minnesota was no exception. Public health preparedness became a paramount concern to the state's citizens and government. The state's two nuclear power plants on the Mississippi River, in Monticello and Prairie Island, caused alarm, as did organizational challenges and legal and policy directions. At the behest of the former commissioner, Jan Malcolm, Aggie convened a task force.

Members of the commissioner's Terrorism and Health Task Force included the FBI, National Guard, fire departments, police departments, Department of Public Safety and the emergency preparedness infrastructure – public health, hospitals, physicians and other health care providers. Coordinating different agendas to reach a common goal was a gargantuan task. Fortunately, Minnesotans in large numbers stepped forward to aid the task force by participating in public forums. The task force's immediate accomplishments were the creation of a new Office of Emergency Preparedness within the Minnesota Department of Health and proposed legislation to address potential emergencies caused by biological or chemical terrorist attacks.

In 2002, the Emergency Health Powers Act passed the state legislature after painstaking collaboration between legislative committees and the Department of Health under Aggie's leadership. The act updated and clarified isolation and quarantine activities and must be reenacted in 2004, when it will face tough questions from some legislators who believe the Department of Health may be vested with too much power. Other legislators may ask whether additional liability insurance is needed to cover volunteers, whether or not volunteers should administer

Conferring with Patricia Bloomgren, director of the Environmental Health Division.

The Faces of Public Health, *Aggie Leitheiser*   93

Observing a demonstration of
the use of a rapid HIV test.

Confering with MDH legislative
coordinator Lin Nelson and
Representative Jim Abeler on
the steps of the state capitol.

In the capitol with
Representative Jim Abeler
before a committee hearing.

Catching up on paperwork.

Learning details of an expanded
newborn screening program with
lab specialist Dan Johnson at the
Public Health Laboratory.

vaccines, and whether quarantine provisions are sufficient.

An unforeseen advantage of the Emergency Health Powers Act has been a renewed focus on the kinds of emergencies the state usually faces, such as annual flooding of the Mississippi and Red Rivers and influenza outbreaks. By rethinking emergency preparedness in anticipation of possible terrorist attacks, and creating an Office of Emergency Preparedness within the Minnesota Department of Health, the state has clarified its approach to the sorts of emergencies it expects to face nearly every year. Minnesota's approach to public health emergencies is now more collaborative and encompassing, the embodiment of "be prepared."

Aggie led the Minnesota Department of Health in responding to the National Smallpox Vaccination Program. She oversaw an evaluation of the consequences of renewed smallpox vaccination and made sure that public health protection principles were implemented. The program became a test of her belief in building local infrastructure and enhancing capacity, and she ensured that grant dollars and staffing choices reflected Minnesota's public health priorities. Regional clinics vaccinated more than 1,500 public health, health care and emergency response staff against smallpox, ranking Minnesota as one of the top states in the nation in this effort. This success reflected the strong state/local and public/private partnerships Aggie put in place to respond to public health emergencies. Regional bioterrorism planners continue to be based throughout the state to work directly with local agencies.

Aggie believes the public health field is full of opportunities. She encourages young people thinking of careers in public health to not limit themselves by choosing a narrowly focused

specialty. Successful careers in public health often come from moving around, as she has done. Being prepared can mean rising to meet challenges from a generalist rather than a specialist point of view.

Ten years from now Aggie sees public health focused once again on infectious disease as well as on chronic disease. Chronic disease will affect more people on a day-to-day basis, but infectious disease will more likely lead to groundbreaking advances, whether through new vaccines or solving the epidemiology of emerging disease.

Aggie Leitheiser's excellent perspective on public health comes from a career that has given her hands-on experience in many different areas. As a manager and leader, Aggie demonstrates a high level of understanding of a diverse set of public health issues. While she has dealt firsthand with many public health programs, she also understands the importance of building good working relationships with local communities, regulated industries, local public health agencies, the state legislature and a variety of state and federal agencies. She recognizes the value of her employees and supports and encourages their development. She encourages doing what is right even when it is unpopular. Above all, she embodies the motto "be prepared." Minnesotans can be thankful for Aggie Leitheiser's public health leadership.

Jean Malecki, MD, MPH

Florida

Demonstrating calm and authority in the face of the nation's anthrax attack

At 3 pm on Oct. 2, 2001, a public health crisis that would shake the nation erupted in Palm Beach County, Fla. Dr. Jean Malecki, Palm Beach County Health Director, received a telephone call from a colleague alerting her that a gravely ill man had been admitted at 2 am that morning to a local hospital. The wife of patient Robert Stevens had driven him all night from a visit to their daughter in North Carolina. At the time of admission, Mr. Stevens was unable to communicate. Two days later, blood tests from the state laboratory in Tallahassee and the Centers for Disease Control in Atlanta confirmed his illness – inhalation anthrax. Fortunately, Dr. Malecki had already started an investigation into the possible causes of Mr. Stevens' illness during that two-day waiting period. The news of the anthrax confirmation broke on Oct. 4, and Mr. Stevens died the next day, Oct. 5.

That day, Dr. Malecki became "the face" of the public health response to the anthrax exposure.

Her calm, collected manner and poise in front of television cameras and microphones were welcome antidotes to the panic and fear caused by the death of Mr. Stevens. Years of training and preparation for just such an incident gave her the confidence and clear thinking to handle the high-profile visibility.

The eldest of four daughters, Jean grew up in West Palm Beach, the very place she has spent most of her career. Jean's father and mother, a physician and a schoolteacher, set influential examples for her. At Fairfield University in Connecticut, she majored in premedical studies with a minor in religion and philosophy. Like many women of the 1970s, she was torn between marriage and a career. Complicating matters, her college adviser told her she would never become a physician. Fortunately, Jean's family and friends encouraged her not to give up the dream of a medical career. In the end, she both married and went to medical school.

Jean embraced her life as a medical student. Attending New York Medical College in Valhalla, New York, Jean had the opportunity to work in urban clinical settings. Metropolitan Hospital in Harlem became her favorite due to the great variety of cases she treated there. Six months before medical school graduation, she gave birth to a daughter, and was back on rounds in less than three weeks. At Honors Day ceremonies before graduation, Jean received three awards and accepted them proudly holding her baby daughter in her arms. Jean finished 10th in her class of 140, determined to have both a family and a medical career.

Jean and her family returned to Florida, where she became a resident in obstetrics and gynecology at the University of Miami School of Medicine. Her marriage ended during this

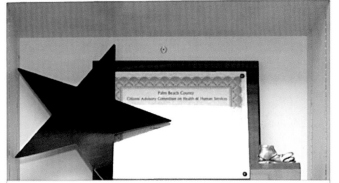
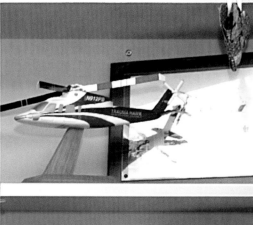

period, and Jean began to dread the thought of the all-consuming work and unpredictable hours of an obstetrician. When she heard that the Palm Beach County Health Department needed someone to run a community health center, she leapt at the chance. Her hours became predictable, allowing her to devote time to her daughter and complete a residency program in preventive medicine. She also earned her master's degree in public health from the University of Miami, paid for by Palm Beach County and completed in 18 months.

Dr. Malecki has now been with the Palm Beach County Health Department for 22 years, 12 of them as director. Of the department's 800 employees, 40 are physicians, most board-certified in preventive medicine. Fortunately, Jean had started preparing teams to deal with terrorist threats as early as 1997. County health workers, joined by local hospitals, fire and police departments throughout the county, the FBI and the CDC, had run joint exercises anticipating possible attacks. They had even practiced responses to a possible anthrax attack. Upon learning of the actual anthrax exposure on that fateful October day, Jean and the County Health Department activated an emergency preparedness script they had practiced before.

Calm and practiced responses to the anthrax threat followed. First, Jean herself met with Mrs. Robert Stevens and interviewed her extensively, pulling together a timeline and a list of contacts. After investigating all the areas where Mr. Stevens worked, lived and spent time, the investigative team found anthrax spores in the American Media International (AMI) building in Boca Raton where he had worked. The building was cordoned off, and Dr. Malecki announced that all employees should be screened at a county office building. At this point, the emergency preparedness force began its work. FBI agents began a careful analy-

sis of the AMI site while CDC officials began to identify the particular anthrax spores that had caused Mr. Stevens' death.

Meanwhile, the health department assembled a team of 80 health professionals to meet with AMI workers on Oct. 7. The health department team began screening 2,000 AMI employees and others exposed in the building five days after Mr. Stevens died, and also prescribed the antibiotic Ciprofloxacin as a precaution. Looking back to that first response plan, Jean wishes she had included mental health professionals as part of the team to handle the many AMI workers who exhibited signs of post-traumatic stress syndrome.

The intense detective work of CDC and FBI officials revealed that the anthrax spores, in a highly concentrated form, came from a letter addressed to AMI that the nearsighted Mr. Stevens had examined close to his nose. Only one secondary case occurred from the anthrax exposure, and it was historic. Mr. Blanco, another AMI employee who worked near Mr. Stevens, had been admitted to a hospital days before with a respiratory complaint and had been treated aggressively with several antibiotics, including Cipro. Only after he was linked to Mr. Stevens did it become known that Mr. Blanco was probably the first person ever to be cured of inhalation anthrax.

Jean believes that first-responder preparedness in the United States has improved dramatically since the anthrax incident in October 2001. Public health departments were already reasonably well-prepared, in her opinion, but hospitals and other health care providers are now much more alert to signs of chemical and bioterrorism. The CDC now makes information more quickly available and continues to improve communications networks that will be vital in countering any terrorist threat.

Despite the high-profile visibility Jean received during the anthrax incident, she does not consider bioterrorism her No. 1 public health concern. Obesity concerns her most. In Palm Beach County, more than 33 percent of children are obese, putting them at great risk for diabetes and its complications: retinopathy, cardiovascular disease and renal failure. Still, Jean feels confident the epidemic can be overcome through consistent, repetitive messages to school-age children and their parents about healthy diets and exercise.

A self-proclaimed optimist, Jean points out that anyone in public health must have a positive, can-do attitude. In order to improve the public's health, a community must band together and challenge the status quo. In the past decade, Palm Beach County has lowered the percentage of pregnant women who do not receive prenatal care from 20 percent to just 2 percent. In that same period, infant mortality rates have declined from 28 percent to 7 percent.

Dr. Malecki advises young people considering a career in public health to innovate, think futuristically and dare to be entrepreneurial. This last quality is especially important in the face of government budget cuts. The Palm Beach County Health Department has 121 funding sources, many of them multiyear foundation and government grants. The department frequently steers funding to community partners – nongovernmental organizations dealing with maternal and child health, asthma, HIV/AIDS and a host of other health concerns. Under Dr. Malecki's leadership, the department built bridges to the private and nonprofit sectors to attack health issues with the full backing of the community. Nongovernmental organizations enlist members of the community to do their work, and if they succeed in reducing health problems, the County Health Department succeeds.

Dr. Malecki in her office with photographs of her daughter, Heather Girardi.

Taking care of paperwork.

Meeting with doctors
Robert Trenschel and
Alina Alonso.

Jean Malecki believes the public health profession will grow in recognition and visibility in the next 10 years. She anticipates that basic infrastructure will be improved and leadership and training advanced. She feels that health departments themselves should be the training sites for preventive medicine, taking over that role from academic research institutions that don't deal directly with public health. The fact that less than half of 1 percent of funding for residence training goes to preventive medicine is unacceptable, in her view, and she advocates for an upsurge in public health resources and in people willing to make public health their career.

On that October day, faced with an anthrax exposure whose reach was yet unknown, Jean responded as a public health professional. She took charge immediately, and responsibly, without dwelling on how her actions would advance the nation's public health preparedness. In fact, they did. Fortunately, years earlier, she had rebelled against the advice of her college adviser and enrolled in medical school. The people of Palm Beach County are grateful she did.

Russell Moy, MD, MPH

Maryland

Creating innovative approaches to maternal and child health

Families in Maryland owe a better quality of life to Russell Moy. In 1989, when Dr. Moy joined the Maryland Department of Health and Mental Hygiene from his private practice in obstetrics and gynecology, infant mortality rates were consistently high. Teen pregnancies and teen smoking, two of the most pressing health issues of adolescents, were also alarmingly high. For Russell, a board-certified obstetrician, the joy of delivering babies was surpassed only by the joy of assuring families healthier lives and encouraging teenagers to aspire to adult lives full of promise. Russell exchanged sterile gloves and the delivery room, where he delivered up to 300 babies a year, for "hands-on" public health programs that directly touched all of Maryland's families and improved their lives.

Russell Moy was born in Washington, D.C., and lived there through seventh grade when his family moved to Silver Spring, Maryland, the largest suburb in Montgomery County. Russell's father was a civil servant who worked his entire career at the Social Security Administration. Russell graduated from Paint Branch High School in 1971 and enrolled at the University of Maryland College Park. For the right price – in-state tuition – he stayed close to home and in touch with his friends, including many who also enrolled at the university. As a pre-medical student, he majored in zoology and after graduating in 1975, enrolled at the University of Maryland School of Medicine in Baltimore.

In 1979, upon graduating from medical school, Russell began a residency in obstetrics and gynecology at the University of Maryland Hospital in Baltimore. He found childbirth fascinating and became intrigued by the blend of medicine and surgery that obstetrics and gynecology affords. During his first year of residency, Russell met and married Debra, a nurse at the Veterans Administration Hospital. They have a son and daughter, both now grown. Debra continues to work as a nurse, now at Blue Cross and Blue Shield.

In 1983, after completing his residency and becoming board eligible, Russell headed to Culpeper, Virginia, to join a medical school friend who was establishing a practice in obstetrics and gynecology. Over the next six years, Russell delivered between 200 and 300 babies a year, an intense practice with every other weekend on call.

Having read on his own about public health, and drawn to the possibility of making an impact on a large population, Russell enrolled at the George Washington University School of Public Health in 1988. He attended classes every other weekend for three years and found the courses invigorating and fun. He earned his master's degree in public health in 1991.

In 1989, while working toward his MPH, Russell had the good fortune to apply and be hired for a rare opening at the Maryland Department of Health and Mental Hygiene, in the Office of Maternal Health and Family Planning. Dr. Carlyle Crenshaw, the chair of his residency program, supported Russell's candidacy even though he had yet to complete his MPH. Although he was a clinician, Dr. Crenshaw had always been attuned to public health. A strong proponent of perinatal regionalization as a strategy for improving pregnancy outcomes, Dr. Crenshaw became an even more important mentor to Russell. In the new job, Russell supervised 30 people and a $10 million budget; 10 years later, his role having grown, he led 250 people and a $250 million budget. Over the years, Russell's duties expanded to include community health, disease control, primary care and oral health as well as oversight of two state hospitals for chronic rehabilitation.

Russell immediately turned his energies to improving pregnancy outcomes. He recognized that Maryland lacked a forum for addressing maternal and infant issues, and helped create the Maryland State Commission on Infant Mortality Prevention. Established by the legislature in 1991, the forum heightens public awareness of infant mortality prevention as well as maternal and infant health in general. The 1991 legislation also focused attention on the need to revitalize Maryland's vital statistics unit. With new expertise, Maryland infant mortality data now becomes available consistently within six months of each calendar year, a quantum improvement from the past. Birth certificates are now linked to infant death certificates and hospitals receive neonatal mortality rates that are matched to specific birth weights, assisting them with quality improvement. Perinatal survey data became available for the

first time, and multiple adverse outcome review processes were implemented for fetal and infant mortality, child fatalities and maternal fatalities by county. As a result, Maryland's perinatal surveillance capabilities have been significantly strengthened over the past 10 years.

Starting in 1989, as soon as he joined the Maryland Department of Health and Mental Hygiene, Russell set out to update clinical standards and guidelines for prenatal care. With the help of academic centers and other perinatal experts, clinical standards and quality assurance processes for prenatal care, family planning care and other reproductive health care were put into place and have been routinely updated ever since. By the mid-1990s, as part of the Maryland Perinatal Health Initiative involving many partners, Maryland reached consensus on perinatal care standards for hospitals. A process for on-site hospital reviews of perinatal units assures the public that hospitals are complying with the standards.

Another of Russell's innovations, the Crenshaw Perinatal Health Initiative, put into place community-based approaches to high-technology issues and education. The initiative established across Maryland high-risk consultation and referral mechanisms, maternal-neonatal transport standards and perinatal care standards. At the same time, the initiative solidified approaches to so-called "high touch" (vs. "high tech") issues. These "high touch" issues included public information, provider education, community coalition building, community-based perinatal health improvement plans, community-based fetal and infant mortality reviews, and community-based child fatality reviews. All of these approaches gave life to Dr. Crenshaw's concept of perinatal regionalization as a strategy for improving pregnancy outcomes.

Russell also needed to address the issue of unintended pregnancies. He did so by creating the Healthy Teens and Young Adults Program. To prevent teen pregnancy, this model program focused on family planning education and services, male involvement in reproductive health decisions, and expanding life options for young people in need. At the same time, a program called Healthy Options for Prevention and Empowerment (or HOPE) made available to low-income individuals the newer, higher cost family planning technologies such as Depo-Provera and Norplant. Preconception health care was emphasized through the Folic Acid Awareness Campaign, designed to heighten public awareness of neural tube defects, genetic disorders and hereditary conditions and ways to prevent them. Finally, Maryland Medicaid's Family Planning Program provided five years of postpartum family planning coverage to women who had been eligible for Medicaid during their pregnancies, but who would otherwise lose eligibility after delivery.

In 1992, after three years at the Maryland Department of Health and Mental Hygiene, Russell felt torn between staying in public health and returning to clinical practice. The abrupt change from delivering babies nearly every day and being closely involved in the reproductive health and pregnancies of the mothers left a void in his life. Also, the pay differential between clinical practice and public health, at a time when he had a growing family of his own, prompted Russell to take a six-month leave of absence. He joined a local hospital as clinical director of obstetrics and gynecology to test whether he should return to full-time clinical practice. However, he soon bridled at decisions he believed gave greater weight to costs than to patient safety, seeing the quality of care suffer in

some cases. After six months, he returned to his public health post with a clear mind and a renewed commitment to his chosen second field. He has never looked back.

In 1999, Russell became the head of a newly organized division of the Maryland Department of Health and Mental Hygiene called Family Health Administration (FHA). FHA has eight major divisions: Maternal and Child Health (his old division), Genetics & Children with Special Needs, Primary Care and Rural Health, WIC (Women, Infants, Children – a federal nutrition program for low income families), Cancer Surveillance & Control (made possible by tobacco settlement money), Health Promotion (smoking cessation, among other programs), Center for Preventive Health Services (chronic disease prevention), and Oral Health. The divisions fit well together, addressing issues relevant to children, adolescents and mothers. They emphasize the importance of viewing maternal health from preconception, acknowledging that precursors of health problems for children often begin even before they are conceived.

Russell's FHA divisions can cite many successes that grew out of innovative approaches to maternal and child health. While Russell's initial focus after joining the department was relatively narrow – improving infant health – his later efforts focused on improving the health of the whole family. The successes include a 27 percent decrease in teen birthrates in the past 10 years and a 66 percent decrease in childhood lead poisoning in the past five years. Tobacco use decreased 12 percent over the past two years among all adults, 22 percent among high school students, and 30 percent among middle school students. Cancer cases decreased 14 percent over the past 10 years, with mortality rates dropping

In front of the Maryland Department of Health & Mental Hygiene.

On the porch with Daisy, a Welsh corgi.

Conferring with colleague David Long.

twice as fast as the rest of the nation. Since 2001, tobacco settlement money has allowed Russell's cancer division to focus on colorectal cancer, increasing demand for colonoscopies by creating more favorable attitudes toward them. As proof of its commitment to community-based, individualized approaches to preventive health care, FHA disperses grants to local health departments and allows them to determine how to proceed.

Russell believes that the general public and elected officials do not fully understand the value of disease prevention. An emphasis on Medicaid and Medicare in Congress over the decades has led to a focus on treatment rather than prevention. The picture is fast changing, however. New metabolic tests make possible early identification of genetic predispositions to certain diseases. Simple prevention techniques such as the screening of infant hearing make early treatment possible and ensure appropriate development. Improved health education to help patients properly manage chronic conditions also contributes to secondary prevention of more serious complications and better health outcomes.

Russell believes that the concept of prevention must be made both understandable and valuable to people. While it seems evident that not enough money exists in the world to pay for all treatments for all diseases for all people, one must have data to make the case. Treatment costs for preventable diseases can be infinite and unpredictable, whereas an investment in prevention can lead to longer, healthier lives. Russell believes the data leave no doubt that prevention works. He further believes that the perception by the general public and government officials toward prevention must be turned around within the next 10 years. For prevention to prevail, this critical window of opportunity to educate and advocate for its benefits must be exploited.

For clinicians contemplating a career switch, as he did, Russell's advice is to recognize public health as a multifaceted discipline. He urges others entering public health not to shrink from developing operational expertise – strategic planning, goal setting, budgeting, personnel management, procurement and information technology cement the structure of large organizations. These aspects of medicine and public health often turn people off, he observes, but must be mastered for a system or organization to thrive. Russell has made a point of mastering three key areas: budgeting, recruiting and retaining staff, and communications. He believes that understanding and effectively managing all three areas is essential to continued growth in the public health field. While his clinical experience played a role in his success, Russell finds that the public health program implementation – population-based screening and health education – and mastery of the operational aspects of running a large department in state government are even more important.

Perhaps most important for a public health professional, or any professional, is having a mentor to guide, counsel and offer encouragement throughout one's education and career. Russell was fortunate to have two such mentors: Dr. Crenshaw and Dr. David Nagey. Unfortunately, Dr. Crenshaw died in an automobile accident in 1995; Russell still misses the advice of this friend and mentor. Dr. Nagey, internationally prominent for his perinatal work at the University of Maryland and later at Johns Hopkins, died of a heart attack while running in a race in 2002. Losing two mentors in the space of eight years has been a blow to Russell. He relied on them as sounding boards for many of his wisest decisions and now passes their experience on as a mentor himself to future generations.

When Russell Moy made the switch to public health from his private clinical practice in obstetrics and gynecology, he was still attached to the rewards of delivering one baby at a time. Fortunately, a mentor spoke up on his behalf and helped him land an important position at the Maryland Department of Health and Mental Hygiene, starting him on his new path in public health. He has learned that population-based approaches to health care have huge rewards. He can take pride in all that he has accomplished in improving the lives of families across Maryland.

Dennis Murray, MPH

Ohio

Piloting new approaches to improving men's health

Women are often viewed as the primary decision-makers in the family when it comes to health and nutrition issues. Many health education initiatives focus on women as the "gatekeepers' for information about proper diet, exercise and preventive health for their husbands and children. A unique pilot program in Ohio, however, focused on men's perceptions of their health and well-being and created an experimental program for educating them about the dangers of obesity and excess weight.

Educating physicians to teach their male patients about the risks of excess body weight, poor diet and lack of exercise was the focus of the Men's Health Awareness Project in Ohio's Knox and Morrow Counties. A team led by Dennis Murray, health commissioner of Knox County, proposed the project to the Ohio Public Health Leadership Institute, becoming one of six projects selected for funding in 2001. His project on men's health responded to an unspoken need in the community, the fact that too many men who were overweight seemed pleased with their well-being and that physicians were ineffective in educating these men about prevention strategies.

As a lifelong Ohioan, Dennis feels committed to the health of the state's residents. He was born in 1957 in Wakeman, Ohio, halfway between Toledo and Cleveland. His father was a local banker. He graduated in 1975 from Western Reserve High School and headed to Kenyon College in Gambier,

Ohio, 100 miles northeast of Columbus and about 75 minutes from his hometown.

At Kenyon, Dennis concentrated on the sciences and mathematics, and in his sophomore year began thinking of health care delivery systems or medical research as a career direction. During spring break of his junior year, he participated in the Kenyon extern program, spending one week at Memorial Sloan Kettering Hospital in New York City assisting a cancer researcher who was studying mice. Dennis realized that he preferred working with people to laboratory research. Because his graduation year, 1979, was very competitive for entry to medical school, he left college undecided about his career direction. He took time to travel the length of Canada and then returned home to Wakeman to begin a job search.

Dennis began researching environmental health and realized that Ohio, a home rule state, had 120 health districts in its 88 counties. Home rule meant that most public health programming began at the local level. His home county, Huron, had no openings but the health department referred him to the Ashland City/County Health Department. Ashland in turn referred him to a state training program in Akron where he accompanied health inspectors (also known as environmental health "sanitarians") in on-the-job training for four months. Ashland provided a small stipend – fortunately, a college friend's family invited him to stay with them near Akron – and guaranteed that once he completed the training he would have a job.

In April 1980, Dennis started work after completing his training. In Ohio, a health inspector must pass a test to become registered but must also work in the field for two years. Dennis worked as a generalist in the environmental health division in Ashland County, one of four on a staff

of seasoned health inspectors responsible for water, wastewater, solid waste, restaurant and food inspection, as well as public schools and campgrounds. Jack Lentz, MPH, RS, the Ashland Public Health Commissioner and a mentor to Dennis, helped him surmount a steep learning curve. Dennis also met and married Bernadette during his stint in Ashland County. She taught at his old elementary school in Wakeman.

In 1984, Dennis transferred to the Medina County Health Department, a larger, more metropolitan area near Akron with greater opportunities for professional growth. Dennis worked in Brunswick and Hinckley, two bedroom communities for workers at a Ford Motors plant and nearby steel mills. In 1986, Dennis entered the University of Michigan School of Public Health as a full-time student to earn his master's degree in public health. Dennis entered the program as a 48-credit-hour student rather than the customary 60 credit hours, his seven years of work experience accounting for the difference. Dennis loved living in Ann Arbor and learned the bus system by heart, leaving the car to his wife for her commute to Manchester, Michigan, where she taught school. Dennis worked part time for almost six months at the National Sanitation Foundation, a testing laboratory in Ann Arbor, but gave up the job when the demands of his full time studies became too much. In addition to Bernadette's teaching income, he took student loans to meet living and tuition expenses.

Dennis graduated with his MPH in December 1987 and set out to find a job that would lead him toward his dream of becoming a health commissioner. His first job was in Livingston County, Michigan, a growing county with many cottages on small lakes. He was one of 15 public health inspectors on staff. Dennis and his wife

wanted to return to Ohio, however, and in 1989 Holmes County, northeast of Knox County, hired him as the environmental health director. He moved with his wife to Millersburg, Ohio, the county seat of the small rural county (population 30,000) with a large Amish population. Their daughter was born in 1989 and their son in 1992. Dennis spent much of his time dealing with Amish families and educating them, as they were skeptical about environmental regulations and wondered why they needed permits for many activities. He was a working director with a staff of three, and was active also in the Ohio Environmental Health Association.

In 1997, Dennis moved to Knox County as environmental health director, reporting to the same commissioner who oversaw Holmes County. He now supervised a staff of five, lessening the need for him to be a working director. Within a month, the commissioner chose to oversee Holmes County exclusively and the Board of Health in Knox County appointed an interim commissioner from the department of nursing. Dennis applied for the job and was appointed commissioner in October 1997. He continued in his role as environmental health director, however, and it was not until 1999 that the board hired a full-time environmental health director to free him from the dual role, which continued until March 2000. Dennis and his family live in Mt. Vernon (population 17,000), the county seat of Knox County, not far from Gambier where Dennis attended Kenyon College.

It was around this time, the year 2000, that the Ohio Public Health Leadership Institute (OPHLI) accepted Knox County and neighboring Morrow County into the Institute to develop a men's health project. Housed in the Ohio Department of Health since 1994, and scheduled to move to the new School of Public Health at

Ohio State University, OPHLI receives its funding from the Centers for Disease Control and Prevention. It solicits nominations from health commissioners and Boards of Health for worthy community-based projects, awarding six to seven grants a year. The awardees form teams to work on public health problems or concerns in their communities and provide midyear and end-of-year status reports to OPHLI. OPHLI aims to encourage professional development and the use of management tools and to broaden community-based public health.

Dennis Murray formed his team in the fall of 2000 with the charge to be far-reaching in its approach to men's health. In addition to public health practitioners from both agencies and other health care professionals, the team included a retired Kenyon College biology professor and an elected county official who had survived prostate cancer. The team selected obesity and overweight, now running a close second to tobacco as the number one cause of preventable death in the United States, as a key area of research and action. With one year allotted for the project, the team concentrated on constructing a survey instrument, distributing it widely, collecting and analyzing the data, and educating physicians to discuss obesity and nutrition with their male patients.

The project used existing print materials and reached men where they would predictably congregate – car shows and golf outings, for example. As an incentive to complete the survey, men were often given something in return, either pamphlets on male-specific health issues, small gifts such as pens, or the chance to enter raffles. In the end, the team collected 445 completed surveys representing 1.4 percent of the male population 18 years and older in the two counties.

Only 116 out of 445 respondents were not overweight, as shown by the standard measure

At the dedication of the new Health Department building, Dennis shakes hands with his mentor, retired health commissioner Jack Lentz.

The Faces of Public Health, *Dennis Murray*   111

Reviewing charts with a nursing supervisor, Rose Rix.

Dr. Robert George, with patient Andrew Crane, at the recently re-opened Safety Net Dental Clinic.

Reviewing plans for a housing subdivision with Randy Pore, regional planning director.

In front of the Health Department.

Speaking to a medical sociology class at Kenyon College.

of a Body Mass Index (BMI) of less than 25.0, while 188 were overweight (a BMI of 25.0 to 29.9) and 140 were obese (a BMI of 30.0 or more). Surprisingly, although 74 percent of the respondents had BMIs of 25.0 or greater, and were thus overweight or obese by the standard measure, 53 percent of the respondents reported satisfaction with their weight, 64 percent believed they ate properly, 66 percent classified themselves as physically active and 78 percent reported satisfaction with their overall well-being.

Although 85 percent of the respondents had health insurance in some form, those lacking insurance tended to be younger. The 76 percent of respondents who had visited a physician within the previous 12 months tended to be older than the respondents who had not. Of the men surveyed, 51 percent stated that their last visit to a physician was for a physical or a follow-up exam. Some form of tobacco use was reported by 35 percent of the respondents, 13 percent consumed two or more alcoholic drinks per day and 8 percent had more than one sexual partner during the previous year. Common health conditions such as heart disease and arthritis affected the work or family life of 46 percent of the respondents, and 66 percent of this group knew they had a family history of such conditions. However, only 33 percent of respondents had been screened for any of the common conditions at a health department, hospital or clinic.

Clearly, the sample population did not sufficiently recognize the risks of excess body weight. The Men's Health Awareness Project shared the results of the survey with physicians practicing in the two counties, encouraging them to have frank discussions with their patients about the risks of obesity and ways to prevent it. The project gave the physicians print materials to distribute to patients as a way to break the ice and help with education. OPHLI funded the project for just one year, as it does all its projects, and when the year was up, team members dispersed. Dennis and his team recognize the need to continue the project in some form if it is to have a long-term impact on the health and well-being of men in Ohio.

Dennis finds public health to be all encompassing for the health and safety of a community. Results are often invisible because effective health education and prevention do their good work quietly, out of the limelight. Dennis loves what he does because it brings results. He takes pride in the fact that when he became commissioner of the Knox County Health Department, he inherited a staff of 37 that has since grown to 50 with an expansion in services and additional responsibilities placed on the agency.

Dennis advises people thinking of careers in public health to give it a try and not to discount it. Excessive monetary rewards won't likely materialize, but for those who really want to help people, public health is the right field. At Kenyon College, a medical sociology course has developed a following among students, and Dennis addresses it each year concerning opportunities in public health. If similar courses are offered at campuses across the country, many more young people may be persuaded to enter public health.

Ten years from now, Dennis predicts public health will be even more of a player in local communities. Health providers will discover that their local health departments have valuable information and resources to share and will seek to strengthen bonds with public health professionals in their communities. The Men's Health Awareness Project is a great example of how public health and health care providers can work together toward a common goal of patient education and disease prevention. Commissioners of local health departments, like Dennis Murray, are at the forefront of that movement.

Lisa Penny, RDH

Idaho

Bringing healthy smiles to kids and adults in rural areas

Many people in Idaho owe their healthy smiles to Lisa Penny. During a 34-year career in public health, Lisa has worked to promote oral health, finding ways to prevent dental disease in a state underserved by dentists and conscious of every tax dollar spent.

Less than half of Idaho's citizens on public water systems have optimum fluoride in their drinking water, putting them at higher risk for dental caries, or tooth decay. Lisa, Oral Health program manager in the Idaho Department of Health and Welfare's Division of Health, works with her colleagues to reduce the prevalence of dental disease through innovative programs whose success helps counter the lack of fluoridation and shortage of dentists. The secret to their success? In a state large in area but small in population, they work closely with public and private partners, bringing oral health programs and services to all the people of Idaho.

Lisa came from neither a public health nor family dental background. A first-generation American, she was born at Hamilton Field near San Rafael, California, where her father served in the U.S. Air Force. When she was young, the family moved to Nampa, in southwest Idaho, and except for her college years, she has lived there ever since. She raised two sons in Nampa and now has one grandson and one granddaughter nearby. One of Idaho's larger towns, Nampa lies 20 miles west of Boise, the state capital, in an area now rich with agriculture but once a desert. Rivers diverted for irrigation make potatoes, sugar beets and other crops possible, creating one of the backbones of Idaho's economy. More recently, firms such as Micron and Hewlett Packard opened plants in the area, injecting the welcome addition of high technology.

Lisa chose to attend Idaho State University in Pocatello, in the southeast corner of the state, and planned to major in art. During her college years, she worked part time as a scientific illustrator in the Paleontology Department, drawing Cenozoic bat teeth and other prehistoric artifacts.

Influenced by the numerous employment opportunities available to dental hygienists, she applied to Idaho State's new bachelor's degree program in dental hygiene and was accepted, graduating in 1970. That June she passed the boards and in October of that year began work at the Idaho Department of Health in Boise as a dental hygienist. She was fortunate to have as mentors her first boss, State Dental Director Dr. Allen R. Cutler II, and later Dr. Thomas Bruck, who became dental director in April 1973. Their counsel and work-related educational opportunities have enabled Lisa to continue to

learn and stay current on new developments in dental public health.

In her first role as a public health dental hygienist, Lisa traveled throughout Idaho conducting "Brush-In" programs, making presentations to elementary school children and guiding them as they brushed with a self-applied high-fluoride paste. In the summer months, she staffed a mobile dental van serving migrant and Head Start children in the agricultural areas of southern Idaho, offering screenings and other preventive services to a population particularly underserved by dentists. Of Idaho's 44 counties, 32 have been designated as dental shortage areas, leaving the state with a serious public health issue.

In 1971, district health departments were established in the seven regions of the state as the primary outlets for public health services. Over the next several years, as dental hygienists were hired in each district, Lisa took on a new role as the State Dental Health Consultant, providing training and technical assistance to the districts and others.

Under the leadership of Dr. Bruck, dental programs for pregnant women, children with special needs, and persons in nursing and shelter homes were established in each of the districts. In 1978, a school fluoride mouth rinse program replaced the "Brush-In." The following year, statewide oral health surveys of school-age children were initiated. Lisa helped develop, coordinate and evaluate these programs, conducted through contracts with the district health departments and funded from the Federal Maternal and Child Health (MCH) Block Grant, state and local funds.

In 1987, Lisa became the Acting Dental Director when Dr. Bruck was promoted to State MCH Director. A job reclassification merged her job responsibilities with those of the dental director, and in 1989 Lisa became the State Oral Health Program Manager, the position she holds today. Over the years, emerging science, political and financial changes have redefined program priorities and spurred new partnerships. One constant is the ongoing partnership with the district health departments, allowing preventive dental services to reach 65,000 Idaho residents each year.

Lisa chairs the Idaho Oral Health Alliance (IOHA), a group of individuals and organizations that she first brought together in 1998. Alliance members work to improve the health of Idahoans by increasing access to preventive and restorative dental services.

Lisa co-chaired Seal Idaho 2000, a statewide project in partnership with the Idaho State Dental Association and other IOHA members. Idaho Governor Dirk Kempthorne highlighted the project, the largest community service effort ever undertaken by Idaho dentists, in his State of the State address and in television ads. Seal Idaho 2000 provided free dental sealants to any second-grade student who needed them. A survey the following year found that the number of Idaho third-graders with sealants increased 10 percent between 1999 and 2001 at low-income schools. Many Idaho dentists continue to offer free sealants through their offices and the American Dental Association's annual Give Kids a Smile Day. Currently, two health districts conduct school sealant projects.

In 2001, Lisa led IOHA members to convene an Oral Health Summit, bringing together health professionals, educators and policy-makers to address the dental access issues confronting Idaho. Through the summit and follow-up meetings, six priority goals were identified for Idaho, one of which is to fluoridate community water systems.

Lisa sees the future of dental public health as resting on evidence-based prevention. She notes that almost all dental disease can be prevented through a combination of community, professional and individual strategies. Lisa hopes that one day Idaho will implement across the state both community water fluoridation and school dental sealant programs, the two most effective population-based dental public health interventions.

Following the 2001 Oral Health Summit, Delta Dental Plan of Idaho, an insurance company, stepped forward to champion fluoridation. In 2003, Delta Dental and IOHA initiated the Healthy Idaho Community Water Fluoridation Project, targeting two high-need communities. This partnership offers hope that more Idahoans will enjoy the benefits of fluoridated water.

In 2002, Lisa secured funding for an early childhood caries (ECC) prevention project for high-risk children aged from birth to five years. Data from the Idaho State Smile Survey shows that efforts to prevent dental caries need to begin early. Through emerging science, a fluoride varnish now available can be applied to newly erupted teeth in very young children. The ECC project provides screening, education and fluoride varnish to participants in the WIC (Supplemental Food Program for Women, Infants and Children), Head Start and Medicaid/SCHIP programs.

In 2003, Lisa applied for and received a State Oral Health Collaborative Systems Grant. The grant will expand ECC prevention efforts to address another priority goal: integrating oral health with primary medical care. The majority of Idaho children, whether poor or affluent, do not see a dentist by their first birthday, although it is recommended. On the other hand, physicians see infants and young children many times during the first years of life. Lisa and her project

Lisa helped Pat Meissner paint this mural commemorating 9/11.

With (l to r) Virginia Pierce, Jane Bruesch, and Carol Kuhl, friends and colleagues from the Oral Health Program past and present.

With her first grandchild, Ty Matthew.

With Elke Shaw-Tulloch, chief of the Bureau of Community and Environmental Health.

Meeting with Dr. David Seegmiller and Lalani Ratnayake from the Central District Health Department.

partners will work with the Family Practice Residency of Idaho, providing technical assistance and on-site training for faculty, residents and staff. Efforts will also be made to build dental and medical community awareness and develop a dental referral network to ensure that the project be sustained.

In recognition of her efforts to improve access to dental care, Lisa received the Idaho Public Health Association Health Professional Award in 2000. She is quick to recognize the role of her colleagues in her success, stating that partnership with them makes possible everything she accomplishes. Lisa also acknowledges her program consultants, Dr. Bruck, now retired, and Dr. A. Riley Cutler III, son of her first boss, for their guidance.

Lisa notes that these are encouraging times for dental public health. The surgeon general's report *Oral Health in America*, released in May 2000, focused attention on the "silent epidemic of dental disease" affecting the nation and the link between oral health and overall health. The result has been increased awareness, advocacy and funding for dental public health efforts.

Lisa advises young people thinking of entering the field of public health that they will be able to help many people in their work, not just a few individuals. As first steps, she recommends talking with dental public health professionals and volunteering in a local health department. Young people will discover, as she has, that the variety of roles in public health keeps the field vital and interesting and well worth pursuing.

Lisa Penny's years of service in Idaho demonstrate how "hands-on" the work of a public health professional can be. She has helped increase access to preventive oral health care throughout her state and has educated a whole

generation of children how to care for their teeth. Thanks to Lisa and her colleagues, a healthy smile for every Idaho child is becoming a reality.

Ellen Phillips-Angeles, MS, CHES

Washington

Working to eliminate health disparities among underserved women

Breast cancer affects as many as one in nine women in the United States who live to the age of 90. It is a leading cause of premature death in women. If diagnosed early and treated aggressively, however, breast cancer becomes largely a survivable disease. Unfortunately thousands of women with low incomes and no health insurance do not benefit from early detection, and for them breast cancer is often a fatal disease. Many of these women avoid mammograms and breast self-exams because of fear of breast cancer and a belief that treatment may be unaffordable if they are diagnosed with the disease. Efforts to reduce breast cancer mortality in this underserved population must include an understanding of cultural differences, socioeconomic realities, and misinformation and myths about the disease, as well as access to diagnostic tools and treatments.

Ellen Phillips-Angeles has made it her mission to reduce and eliminate health disparities among underserved women. Her program, the Washington Breast and Cervical Health Program (WBCHP), based in Public Health – Seattle and King County, is dedicated to reducing mortality and morbidity from breast and cervical cancer through early detection of cancer with regular mammogram and Pap test screening exams. The WBCHP serves women with low incomes and no health insurance who are from 40 to 64 years of age. Program services are provided by community-based organizations, with Public Health – Seattle and King County the prime contractor. Funding flows from the Centers for Disease Control and Prevention (CDC), Washington state and local government, and from the Puget Sound affiliate of the Susan G. Komen Breast Cancer Foundation. Funding is never a given, however, and Ellen has become a tireless advocate for her program, working to overcome money hurdles to bring much-needed services to her community.

Washington state currently has the highest rate of breast cancer in the United States, although not the highest mortality rate. The earlier the stage when diagnosed, the better the prognosis for long-term survival of breast cancer, a clarion call for programs like Ellen's. Mortality rates in Washington state have in fact decreased by 33 percent for women first diagnosed over age 50 and by 17 percent for women first diagnosed over age 40 since Ellen joined the WBCHP.

Ellen became the manager of the WBCHP in 1996, having been a public health educator from 1981 to 1996 in Seattle and King County concentrating on women's health, reproductive health, breast-feeding and smoking cessation. As a former VISTA volunteer, Ellen knows that funding and resources are key components of any program's success. With the WBCHP, she oversees

not just the clinical work but also the budget. When faced with a tight budget, as she currently is, she grits her teeth and makes the best of it. One of Ellen's challenges is for the program to become self-sustaining through grants in the face of a decline in funding from local government. King County's tax revenue is shrinking, for example, as more and more small cities incorporate, removing themselves from the county's revenue mix. In 2003, the WBCHP provided 5,260 screenings compared to 4,837 in 2002, a significant jump in services despite a challenging funding environment.

Ellen was born in Flint, Michigan, the middle child of three with an older sister and younger brother. Her mother taught school before becoming a school librarian, and her father, an accountant, worked as a manager at the Chevrolet engine plant in Flint. She attended schools in the Carmen School District and graduated from Ainsworth High School. In high school, Ellen realized she loved biology, and her teacher, Mr. Bourn, arranged an internship for her at Hurley Hospital in a lab run by his wife. Ellen remembers the impact the book *The Other Side of the Mountain*, about a skier overcoming an injury, had on her. When she enrolled at the University of Michigan in 1971, she intended to major in physical therapy.

Ellen felt overwhelmed by the size and competitive environment at the University of Michigan in Ann Arbor, especially in the hard sciences. As she took her courses, her interests moved beyond physical therapy. She chose to major in practical botany, a newly established major that did not require any additional study of organic chemistry.

As a newly minted University of Michigan graduate with a degree in botany, Ellen chose

neither to continue studying botany at the master's degree level nor to work as a landscaper, another option for a botany major. Instead, she joined VISTA (Volunteers in Service to America) in Cleveland, Ohio. Assigned to a health project in the Near West Side near the steel mills, she coordinated a free clinic and received $110 a month for living expenses. She recruited doctors, nurses and other health care workers and ran a women's education group. During her year's service, Ellen became an accomplished health organizer, finding ways to work with such dissimilar populations as Puerto Ricans, eastern Europeans, Appalachians and southern blacks. She roomed with another volunteer in the Tremont neighborhood and counts that roommate among her best friends to this day.

The environmental degradation in her Cleveland neighborhood appalled Ellen. The nearby steel mills emitted air pollutants, the Cuyahoga River caught fire, and the gritty streetscapes lacked trees and other amenities to soften them. Poor people in desperate situations populated the Near West Side. Working with many others, Ellen approached the Cleveland Department of Health to advocate for clinics that could make a lasting contribution to the population. A year after she departed the Tremont neighborhood, a clinic did open there and survived for 20 years.

During her VISTA stint, the promise of the health education field opened Ellen's eyes to career possibilities. She met a former VISTA volunteer, Ranesto "Ron" Angeles, who was studying for a master's degree in social work at Case Western Reserve University after serving a year earlier in the same Tremont neighborhood. Originally from Seattle, Ron intended to return there, and when he did, Ellen followed. In fact, over the years, Ellen's entire family moved from Michigan to Washington state and now lives nearby. Ellen

applied to the health education program at the University of Washington (known in Seattle as U Dub) to study for her master's degree. The program at U Dub, run like an MPH program, encouraged students to do fieldwork and arrive at their own theories. Once she entered the program, Ellen spent two and a half years completing the degree. She researched adult-onset epilepsy, interviewed six people in depth, and wrote her thesis from the perspective of grounded theory, i.e. in the words of the actual people she interviewed. She received her M.S. degree in health education in March 1980 and worked as a health educator at Ballard Community Hospital in Seattle before joining the local public health department in Seattle, officially known as "Public Health – Seattle and King County," in 1981.

Meanwhile, Ellen and Ron married in 1979. Ron had earned his bachelor's degree in community health education from Central Washington State University and worked as a health educator in South King County. Ron now works for the City of Seattle managing a Little City Hall in one of Seattle's diverse neighborhoods. He and Ellen live in the Rainier Beach neighborhood of south Seattle and have two daughters, Siri and Antonia. Siri just graduated from U Dub, and Antonia is about to enter Seattle University.

When Ellen received her promotion in 1996 to manage the Washington Breast and Cervical Health Program (WBCHP) in the Women's Health Unit of Public Health – Seattle and King County, her many years as the leading public health educator working with women's health were recognized. King County has 1.6 million people, with 600 thousand living in Seattle proper, but the WBCHP covers four counties – King, Clallam, Jefferson and Kitsap – and in this way is unique among programs in the department. The three counties other than King, all in the "West End" (i.e., on

the Olympic Peninsula across Puget Sound from Seattle) have a population that contrasts with Seattle's. Rural communities predominate, not the packed-in urban and suburban communities of King County.

Ellen's group provides services through a combination of fixed sites (clinics) and mobile vans that perform mammogram and Pap smear test screenings free of charge in underserved neighborhoods. Among the populations the WBCHP targets, African-American women suffer the greatest mortality from breast cancer. Other priority populations are lesbians, Latinas, Asians, Pacific Islanders and Native Americans, particularly the Makah tribe on the Olympic Peninsula. Since preventive screening is considered unusual in many cultures, Ellen and her staff spend much of their time leading workshops in women's health to build awareness about the benefits of screening and to dispel myths. Such myths include fears of radiation and concerns about painfulness. For women who are found to have suspicious lesions or results from Pap tests, the WBCHP links with partner agencies to provide follow-up treatment.

Ellen edited curricula for teaching about women's health, particularly sexual health, in grades K-12, which Public Health – Seattle and King County published. In addition, she co-authored a curriculum guide on women's health for grades K-4. The guides are used in schools throughout Seattle and the surrounding counties. She also worked on a breast-feeding promotion project, funded by the CDC, and co-authored and published *Breast-Feeding Triage Tool*, a book widely distributed in Seattle and beyond.

The WBCHP has a staff of seven (some part time) and 50 contractors serving 55 to 60 primary care locations. In 2001, Ellen advocated in the Washington State Legislature for legislation that

A Public Health staff meeting with, from left: Donna Cruse Adler, Jodi Olson, Scott Feest, Claire Magbanua, Barb Tiller, Ellen, Ranesto "Ron" Angeles, Roxana Chen, and Deanne Boisvert.

Ellen with her
kitten Penny.

Discussing WBCHP contract budgets with Scott Feest.

Walking up the hill to
Harborview Hospital.

Ellen, the Mariner's fan,
at Safeco Field.

A family vacation in Maui
with daughters Antonia (l)
and Siri, and husband Ron.

allows WBCHP clients who are diagnosed with breast or cervical cancer to be Medicaid-eligible. Prior to this legislation, many women were unable to pay for treatment. Ellen is co-principal investigator for a Department of Defense grant that seeks to identify reasons why African-American women found eligible for the WBCHP decide not to have mammograms. Ellen also serves on the clinical faculty of the University of Washington's Department of Health Sciences. She has won many honors during her career, most recently the Director's Award from Public Health – Seattle and King County in 2004.

Ellen advises others who are thinking of careers in the public health field that job satisfaction is guaranteed. Anyone who enjoys helping others and making a difference will thrive in public health and improve their self-awareness in the bargain. Ellen compares the work she does to coming to a round table – resources are laid out on the table and you get to choose which ones to use and how to use them. Your decisions are most effective, however, if you choose a team approach and work collaboratively.

Ellen would like to be optimistic about public health's future and hopes that the government leaders responsible for resource allocation will restore resources to where they were 20 years ago. Otherwise, she is concerned that a large percentage of the population will not have access to health education, prevention, screening and subsequent treatment. She also has concerns about Washington state's ability to conduct surveillance and disease detection. While no one questions that good public health surveillance prevents disease, it is largely invisible and often suffers cuts during budget retrenchments. Ellen foresees a tug of war ahead between health promotion to address chronic diseases and core infectious disease programs.

The increased incidence of breast cancer since 1940 still perplexes medical researchers, Ellen points out. Family histories – i.e. genetic predisposition – and obesity are known factors, but environmental toxins such as pesticides and organochlorides, although thought to have an impact, have not yet been proven conclusively to cause breast cancer. Ongoing genetic research with Ashkenazi Jewish women, a population especially prone to breast cancer, has identified two genes – BCRA1 and BCRA2 – that are thought to be indicators. Although the test for these genes is currently very expensive, it could be made widely available in four to five years, helping to identify women most at risk for breast cancer and leading to early diagnosis. Ellen hopes that research breakthroughs could move beyond early detection and perhaps even prevent breast cancer.

As a VISTA volunteer with an "impractical" undergraduate major in practical botany, and as a health educator who has made improving women's health her life's work, Ellen Phillips-Angeles makes a difference for the population in and around Seattle. As a wife, proud mother and program manager, she balances home and work and shows that one citizen can improve the health and quality of life of those around her. Every day that Ellen manages the Washington Breast and Cervical Health Program, she measures progress in the cases her team detects and treats early and the suffering and mortality from the disease they prevent among underserved populations. She takes pride in the contributions her team makes to the public's health.

Janet Realini, MD, MPH

Texas

Giving Texas teens a sense of WORTH

San Antonio and Bexar County, Texas, have been home to Dr. Janet Realini since she left her native city of San Francisco in 1975. After 20 years of a successful academic career in family medicine, Jan took the bold step of shifting her career into public health. Her career move tells a story of how love for her community – San Antonio – led her to new commitments that stretched her known boundaries. By moving into public health, she has been able to overcome resistance in the community to workable solutions and contribute to the public's health in ways far more profound than family medicine allowed her.

Born in San Francisco, Jan grew up in that city and attended public schools. She entered the University of California Berkeley in March 1968 after graduating from George Washington High School at age 17. She first considered a career in medicine in her second year of high school when Dr. Theodor Binder, a German physician, visited her church seeking support for his hospital in the jungles of Peru. She saw medicine as a way to combine her strengths in science and academics and help other people.

In the summer of 1970, Jan traveled to Peru to assist Dr. Binder at his hospital in Pucallpa in the Amazon basin. She found the work meaningful and admired how modern health care made such a difference in the lives of a remote, underserved population. However, Jan also realized that life in a jungle did not suit her. Happy to be back at Cal Berkeley, she majored in zoology and applied to medical schools in her third year.

Jan entered the University of California San Francisco (UCSF) Medical School, graduating in 1975. Along with several UCSF classmates, she applied to residency programs in family medicine in San Antonio. She not only matched at the University of Texas Health Sciences Center, she settled down in San Antonio and went on to make her career there in academic medicine.

Jan quickly came to love the city and grew close to the Mexican-American community, admiring the way they demonstrated loyalty, forgiveness and patience, qualities she valued herself. She married Dr. John Holcomb, a pulmonary and critical care specialist and alumnus of Texas A&M University whose Aggie connections span several generations. Jan has two grown stepdaughters and two sons currently attending college in Texas.

In 1979, after completing her residency and a one-year stint at an urban health initiative clinic in San Antonio, Jan joined the faculty of the Department of Family Practice at the University of Texas Health Science Center (UTHSC) in San Antonio. Balancing work and family was important to Jan, so she worked 60 percent of the time when her sons were young. During her academic career, she taught residents and medical students, saw patients, conducted research, published journal articles, ran the residency program for three years and participated fully in the life of the university.

Throughout her career, Jan has been the first woman or one of a very few to achieve leadership roles in what was a male-dominated profession. She was the first woman elected to the Board of Directors of the American Board of Family Practice, serving from 1986 to 1991. She also served as the first woman – and the first woman chair – on the Accreditation Council for Graduate Medical Education's Residency Review

Committee for Family Practice. Her success in these positions helped pave the way for a new generation of women in leadership roles in the world of academic medicine.

Never content with the status quo, Jan began taking classes in San Antonio in public health in 1993, and a year later earned her MPH degree from the School of Public Health of the University of Texas Health Sciences Center in Houston. Her fellow students in the MPH program came from divergent professions, and Jan enjoyed the lively exchanges and different points of view. As she became immersed in public health, Jan compared the number of people wise public health policy affects to a physician seeing one individual at a time in an office or hospital visit. "Everyone, everywhere, everyday," the motto of public health, impressed her greatly. Although she continued as a professor of family practice at UTHSC San Antonio, she eyed opportunities to put her public health training to use. She especially felt the need to do something to address the extraordinarily high rate of teen pregnancy in San Antonio.

In 1998, Dr. Fernando Guerra, director of the San Antonio Metropolitan Health District, hired Jan as medical director of the District's Family Planning Program. Energized by her work with women, she helped found Project WORTH ("Working On Real Teen Health"), an innovative program to address teen pregnancy, in 2000.

To support Project WORTH, Jan forged a working coalition among seven departments in the city government to help the youth of San Antonio make healthy choices. While teaching that abstinence and contraception are both important, Jan believes that the overall outlook for an adolescent is even more important. The concept of youth development – building developmental "assets" and connections with caring adults – is a less controversial starting

point for communities, and youth development became a key focus of prevention efforts of Project WORTH.

Since its inception in 2000, Project WORTH has helped to reduce teen pregnancy in San Antonio and surrounding Bexar County by emphasizing abstinence, parent communication, and positive youth development, while including birth control and sex education as well. Through the efforts of Project WORTH and others in San Antonio, Bexar County's rate of births to school-age girls (15- to 17-year olds) dropped 26 percent, from 58.9 per 1000 in 1994 to 43.5 per 1000 in 2002. Still, this rate is far too high – nearly twice the national rate. Because teen pregnancy is so complex, Project WORTH uses a variety of approaches. Working with community-based organizations, the faith community and the

media, including a popular hip-hop radio station and local Fox and WB television affiliates, Project WORTH has helped persuade growing numbers of youths to begin making wise decisions about sexual activity. Educational programs for youth, parents and city staff are key to outreach efforts. The project distributes fact sheets, detailed teen pregnancy reports and sponsors many events, including annual Teen Health & Career Fairs, a hip-hop song contest, a mayoral proclamation, a teen pregnancy data press conference, and neighborhood WORTH parties.

In coordinating a media campaign to promote abstinence, Jan and her staff of four evaluated several options before settling on "Not Me, Not Now," a creation of the Department of Health in Monroe County (Rochester), New York. This positive, upbeat message from kids to other kids

The Project WORTH (Working On Real Teen Health) clinical staff, Cyndi Morin (l) and Rosie Parrilla.

Communing with a young patient
(Noah) at the clinic.

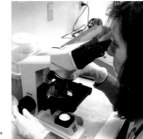
Examining a "wet prep."

Talking with an adolescent.

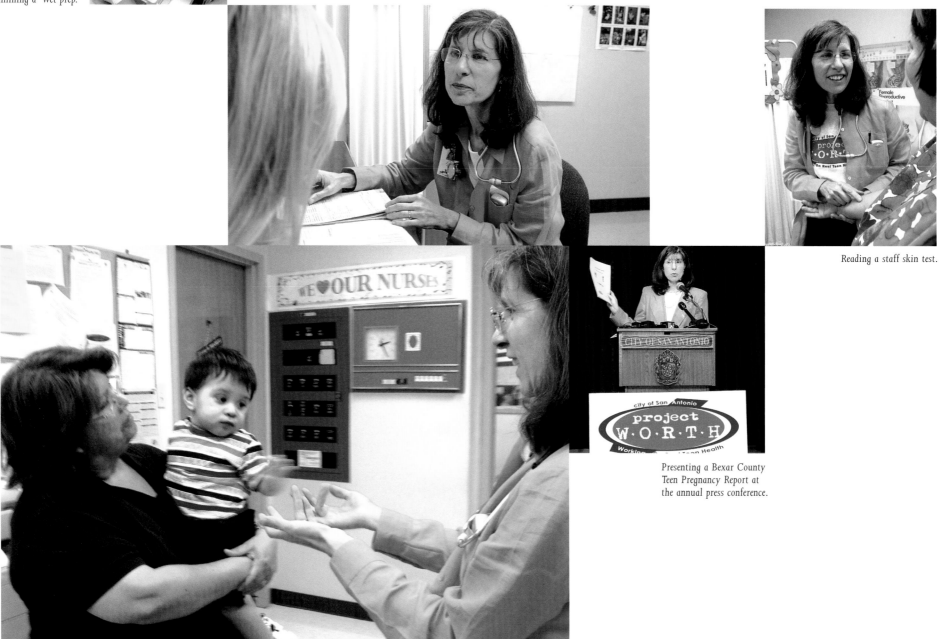

Reading a staff skin test.

Presenting a Bexar County
Teen Pregnancy Report at
the annual press conference.

Enjoying working with children.

focuses on goals and dreams. In 2003, Project WORTH created its own "Waiting is WORTH it!" television and radio spots, continuing the focus on the positive.

Project WORTH promotes an "Abstinence Plus" approach to combat teen pregnancy. While Jan believes that abstinence can work for large numbers of teens and should be widely promoted, she recognizes that those who are sexually active require information and access to birth control. In addition to its message about abstinence, Project WORTH teaches sexually active youth how to avoid sexually transmitted diseases (STDs) and how to use birth control to prevent pregnancy. Unfortunately, the youth at greatest risk are often in greatest need of outreach efforts.

Project WORTH emphasizes connections to family, school and houses of worship as a means to help teens navigate peer pressure and avoid unhealthy risk-taking. Jan points out that when teens feel that they are personally religious they draw on that strength, which helps them feel positive about the future and avoid risky behavior. In promoting an "Abstinence Plus" approach, Project WORTH works with both ends of the cultural divide – abstinence only vs. abstinence as just one strategy – and has found middle ground between conservatives and liberals.

Janet Realini believes that public health will grow in importance over time. Success depends on infrastructure and she hopes government will allocate even greater resources. For each dollar spent on public health measures, the impact on the population is so much greater than through clinical medicine alone. Jan sees the public's recognition of the need for public health as solidifying its future. Even when services are limited, public health turns no one away, and by promoting prevention, helps alleviate the demand for costly emergency medical care.

Jan advises young people to consider public health as a career choice and those not so young to consider a change in careers, as she did, and try to make the greatest difference in their communities. A young person confronting a problem that needs attention should ask, "What can I do?" and secure training to help solve the problem. Public health's focus on prevention and changing behavior in entire populations costs much less in the long run than one on one medical care. Jan's experiences in both fields have given her a unique perspective on what it takes to be successful at tackling society's health problems. And she's happy that her work benefits San Antonio, the city she loves.

Denise Terrell Rondeau

New Hampshire

Stemming a disease outbreak through investigative epidemiology

How Denise Rondeau, a southerner from Florida, helped stem a disease outbreak in New Hampshire is a story worth telling. Although she plans to retire years from now in her native Florida, the people of New Hampshire can be grateful she belongs to them for now. Demonstrating resolve and grace under pressure, two traits that are key to the success of any public health professional, Denise can take pride in how she made a difference with her quick and selfless intervention.

In 2003, when the State Department of Health and Human Services in New Hampshire faced an outbreak of syphilis, Denise and two co-workers stepped forward to plug gaps in the state's public health infrastructure. Denise's role in containing the outbreak came about because of an odd confluence of events. The 16-year veteran chief of the state's STD/HIV Prevention Bureau resigned, leaving Denise as the senior employee in charge. Just as she assumed unexpected administrative duties, and shortly after the chief's departure, the first syphilis case was reported. As it happened, the only other full-time employee in the STD/HIV Prevention Bureau had also recently departed.

The syphilis outbreak began in March 2003 with the case of an 18-year-old female presenting with symptoms. By July, the outbreak had grown to 17 confirmed cases, the greatest number of cases in New Hampshire since the early 1990s and a cause of great concern because unconfirmed cases were likely lurking. Because syphilis can be a harbinger of HIV/AIDS when it presents in gay and bisexual men, a rapid response is needed to contain its spread.

Denise sprang into action, identifying two co-workers from other bureaus and enlisting them to assist in the vital work of contact tracing. She first provided them with an abbreviated training course in STD disease investigation skills. The three then traveled in different directions across the state to locate, notify, interview and re-interview every possible contact to the index and secondary cases. Even more notably, they handled their meticulous, rapid work without missing a beat in their regular work. Their efforts prevented further spread of the disease and the development of a full-blown syphilis epidemic.

Denise and her two colleagues concentrated on tracing contacts, investigative work that often took them into unsafe neighborhoods. In order for contact tracing to work, clients must willingly identify their sexual partners and provide information about how to locate them. While the clients' identities are never revealed, their partners are approached and educated about changing behavior, usually face to face. Denise loves this part of her work, pursuing leads wherever they take her and tactfully communicating in a way that convinces partners to change their risky behavior and seek screening or treatment. In addition to syphilis, other STDs that are traced in New Hampshire are chlamydia, gonorrhea and HIV. All can be spread rapidly through unprotected sex. This represents a constant challenge to contact tracers who must work quickly to identify, treat and in turn prevent new cases, thereby containing an epidemic before it spreads out of control.

The State Department of Health and Human Services in New Hampshire was fortunate to turn to Denise, fully trained in this work in Florida, to contain the syphilis outbreak. Had Denise not stepped into the breach, had she not trained and directed colleagues as fellow investigators, had she not followed through with commitment and concern, the outbreak would have become a far more serious threat to the public's health in New Hampshire and bordering states.

Most people are not familiar with Dunnellon, Florida, where Denise grew up as the eldest of five children. Dunnellon is near Ocala in northern Florida, two hours south of the Georgia border. Her family home stood among a cluster of similar homes in a 10-block development surrounding an old paper mill, an outpost whose population was entirely black. A commitment to school work landed Denise at the University of Florida, an hour's drive away from her home. Coming from an extremely close family, Denise returned home every weekend during college, courtesy of her mother, who drove each way to pick her up and drop her off. Not until her senior year of college did Denise actually spend a weekend in Gainesville apart from her family.

Denise majored in psychology at the University of Florida, concentrating on adolescent developmental psychology. Immediately after graduation in 1988, she returned to Dunnellon and took a job as a substitute band teacher at her old high school where she had played the clarinet. The job lasted two weeks – the unruly high school students drove her to pursue another career. She had kept her eyes posted on the help wanted ads and was fortunate to land a job with the Marion County Health Department in her local county. As all county health departments in Florida are

With her sister-in-law Emma Besso Terrell during the Christmas holidays.

affiliated with the State Department of Health and Rehabilitative Services, Denise became a state employee. Her mother, a school bus driver who became the area coordinator, had raised her to believe that working for the state was the best possible job, bringing long-term security to a family.

Denise began work in Marion County Health Department as a general social worker. After a year and a half, she became an HIV case manager, and then a program coordinator with responsibility for all AIDS programs. After four years, she moved to the District Office in Wildwood, just before the Department of Health and Human Services was reorganized. After the reorganization, she was transferred to the Alachua County Health Department, in the neighboring county surrounding Gainesville, and became program manager for HIV/AIDS surveillance.

While she was still at the Marion County Health Department, Denise enrolled in the non-resident program of the University of South Florida in Tampa to earn a master's degree in public health (MPH). She took all her coursework locally on Friday evenings and Saturdays and over the years earned 27 of the required 36 credits.

In October 1998, Denise moved to New Hampshire to join her husband, Richard, a native of New Hampshire. They had been introduced in Florida by one of Denise's clients. Richard had returned to his home state to start a business and for 14 months Denise continued to work in Florida, becoming vested in the state's retirement system while visiting her husband with their toddler son only on occasional weekends. Today, Denise has a grown stepson, a son in elementary school and twin daughters in preschool.

When Denise finally arrived in New Hampshire in 1998, she did not have a job. She began work as a teacher's assistant in a local school district, pending certification as a permanent substitute teacher. Within six weeks Denise moved to the New Hampshire State Department of Health and Human Services in Concord, once again a state employee. The department assigned

CDC Project Officer Walter Chow and Denise during a team building exercise.

her to help with immunizations, and after a year she transferred to the STD/HIV Prevention Bureau, her true calling. In March 2003, she became program planner for HIV Prevention Services, the position she currently holds.

Denise views public health as providing the last, best hope for many people. She believes that her greatest challenge as a disease investigative

Denise with her co-workers at the STD/HIV Prevention Bureau (l to r) Robert LaChance, Barbara Downes, Priscilla Newton, Patty Melycher, Heather Hauk, and Andrew Thomits.

The Faces of Public Health, *Denise Terrell Rondeau*   135

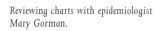

Reviewing charts with epidemiologist
Mary Gorman.

Born in Florida,
Denise's son Drew
builds his first
snowman.

Denise holds her twins Amber (l)
and Kayla (r), now four,
at their first birthday party.

specialist is to help people, often destitute, put aside their pride and embarrassment to save the lives of others. In her view, they have no other recourse. By treating them with as much dignity and respect as possible, Denise can encourage these people to change risky behavior. Denise

Moving north, and saying goodbye to co-worker Patty Carnuccio.

loves what she does and finds the work very rewarding. For her, each day pays dividends for the public's health.

Ten years from now, Denise expects that the public health infrastructure will have expanded. She foresees an emphasis on improved reporting, communication and bioinformatics but hopes that core services for communicable diseases – her specialty – will not be lost. She believes level funding – no allowance for inflation or demand for increased services from year to year – could be disastrous for the effectiveness of public health. Denise hopes a strong voice will emerge to advocate on behalf of public health. That voice must sell people on the need to invest in public health, a challenge the field will always confront.

For now, Denise Terrell Rondeau can take pride in her contributions to the public's health in New Hampshire. By going beyond her routine duties and selflessly taking on unexpected tasks, she made a difference. By rallying support through her can-do attitude, she contained a potential

epidemic. Denise, who like so many before her came to public health to make a difference for those who have no other recourse, exemplifies the best in the field.

Monserrate Salichs, RN, MS

Puerto Rico

Building trust and improving care in Puerto Rico

Playa de Ponce, Puerto Rico, has not been the same since Monserrate Salichs arrived. In 1978, when the government decided to close down the Playa de Ponce Health Center (PPHC), an administratively challenged and financially ailing clinic serving this poor harbor community in the peripheries of Ponce, Monserrate Salichs was hired for a six-month contract to supervise the close down. Instead, she not only saved the clinic but also enlarged it by increasing services to a population she had grown close to, in a community once so proudly insular it spurned even helping hands.

In rescuing the clinic, Monserrate rose to the challenge posed by her mentor and friend, Sister Isolina Ferre, known as the "Angel of La Playa." Today, the Playa de Ponce clinic has 198 employees, up from 86 in 1978. Most significantly, the clinic has immunized 98 percent of Playa de Ponce's children, a remarkable achievement in a community so reluctant to accept help from the outside.

None of this could have happened without the leadership of Monserrate Salichs. Born in 1926 in Ponce, the larger city of which Playa de Ponce (the waterfront section) is a part, Monserrate graduated from Ponce High School in 1946 and held a nurse internship at Doctor Manuel de la Pila Hospital until 1948. In 1949, she co-founded the first oncology clinic in the area with a radiologist from France. In 1950 she began work as a nurse at Doctor Pila Hospital, over the years

developing a unique managerial style as she rose from floor nurse to general nurse supervisor and assistant to the hospital director. In 1958, she graduated from Catholic University as a registered nurse, and in 1964 earned a master's degree in administration, also from Catholic University. She did this while continuing her rise at Doctor Pila Hospital, which she served for 30 years. Her career in health care and public health now spans almost 60 years, and she has no intention of slowing down.

Upon arriving in Playa de Ponce in 1978, Monserrate immediately saw that closing PPHC would devastate the community. Many of the 20,000 residents of Playa de Ponce, located on Puerto Rico's south coast, lived below the poverty line and depended on the clinic for the little health care they got. Having been sent to shut down the clinic, Monserrate immediately challenged the government's indictment that the clinic was economically unviable and lacking in quality of service. On the contrary, Monserrate saw the opportunity to create a true model for community-based health care, one that could quickly become economically viable with services to rival other institutions. She turned to the federal government for help, lobbying the Public Health Administrative Offices to assist with fringe benefits and other financial support that would make PPHC attractive to employees.

But first, before any help arrived from the federal government and facing a three-month turnaround time, she met with the staff and let them know she expected everyone to work hard and save the clinic. Faced with her no-nonsense approach and the uncertain future of the clinic, a number of employees resigned. In fact, the staff of the laboratory resigned en masse, leaving Monserrate no choice but to outsource a critical function. In doing so, she quickly improved both

quality and cost efficiencies. Faced with the loss of 37 staff members overall, Monserrate rallied the remaining staff to improve the clinic's services and rededicate themselves to serving a community in need.

To accomplish her vision, Monserrate did not stop at the borders of Playa de Ponce but instead expanded into other low-income sectors in Ponce, opening three satellite clinics and earning the allegiance of a broad swath of Ponce's population. At the same time, she never gave up on securing more land for the original clinic in Playa de Ponce, and in 1998 succeeded at getting the government to purchase an adjacent six-acre lot for future expansion.

Expanding services has been the watchword for PPHC under Monserrate's direction. In addition to rudimentary services addressing primary care, over time the clinic offered clinical preventive services such as breast cancer screening, echocardiograms, Holter monitors and optometry. It expanded to include ambulatory surgery and transformed itself into an emergency center. The clinic also created a specialized clinical unit for the detection and treatment of HIV/AIDS. Other services include Pro Bono, a legal assistance program for patients, and Project Ray of Light, a drug, alcohol and crime prevention project. Monserrate also instituted a foster grandparents program and a senior companions program.

Not content to restrict the clinic to this impressive array of services, Monserrate and PPHC sponsored the building of a five-story, 84-unit apartment complex for economically disadvantaged senior citizens. The disadvantaged elderly have always been a focus of Monserrate's public health consciousness. The complex overlooks the Plaza del Caribe, southern Puerto Rico's prime commercial center, and the first seniors are

scheduled to move into their apartments by mid-2004. As the complex opens, Monserrate aims to increase clinic hours to round-the-clock, having already expanded opening hours to 16 hours a day.

Thanks to Monserrate's tenacious leadership, the people of Playa de Ponce and other sectors in Ponce are far healthier than they would otherwise have been. Federal and state governments have recognized PPHC's 98 percent immunization record for excellence in health service programs. Despite economic ups and downs – Puerto Rico currently suffers from a 15 percent unemployment rate – Monserrate has kept PPHC running at peak efficiency, serving more than 60,000 patients and dispensing 250,000 prescriptions a year. The

staff holds steady with dedicated, certified professionals who serve those sectors of Ponce with large numbers of people below the poverty line.

What hooked Monserrate on a career in health care, and later in her life, transformed her into a tenacious advocate for public health? When she was 12 years old, her grandmother suffered a stroke and was admitted to the hospital for a long-term stay. Every day, Monserrate prepared ice cream at home and went to the hospital to feed her grandmother. She befriended other elderly patients who had nobody visiting them, wishing she could make them better at the same time as she lifted their spirits. She realized that other relatives did not take care of their sick, a

With her staff in the clinic pharmacy.

Speaking with her son, Allan.

Listening to the phonograph with her grandson, Allan.

Monserrate relaxing.

In front of the Ponce Firehouse with a colorful carnival mask.

Three generations enjoy an evening together.

rude awakening to the challenges of health care and an awakening of her desire to provide care to those who were left alone and forgotten.

Monserrate was fortunate to have had strong personal support for her work from her husband of 52 years, now deceased, and two sons. She met her husband, an accountant, when she was preparing for induction into the U.S. Army. Having passed the physical and on the verge of induction, she chose instead to be pursued by the man who would marry her. Later, in her work at the Doctor Pila Hospital, she came under the spell of Sister Isolina, the legendary Catholic nun who selflessly served the less fortunate in Ponce. It was Sister Isolina who asked Monserrate to join the PPHC board, and when the clinic's future seemed bleakest, in 1978, it was Sister Isolina who entreated Monserrate to become executive director and save it. Monserrate never knew Sister Isolina to close her door and say no to people in need. By always keeping her own door open, by listening to people, and by doing her best to solve their problems, Monserrate honors Sister Isolina in her own work

Monserrate, known by her nickname "Chunga" to her friends and the Playa de Ponce community, believes that young people entering the public health profession should devote themselves first to a community. They should sit down with people and listen to them carefully, spending enough time with them to truly know their needs.

Chunga's dreams for Playa de Ponce include a shelter for the homeless and a new focus on the needs of children with learning disabilities. Too often the homeless are ignored, and children with special needs are referred from place to place, too distant from their own community. By showing the people of Playa de Ponce she would fight for them, and by patiently wooing them with a growing number of PPHC services, Monserrate

Salichs transformed the community. People who were aloof warmed to Chunga's combination of toughness and tenderness, and because she took the time to get to know them, and never gave up on them, they can look forward to living much healthier lives.

144

Dean Sienko, MD

Michigan

Protecting the health of troops while serving his nation

The Kuwaiti desert became home base for Dr. Dean Sienko in March 2003, two days after military forces from the United States and the United Kingdom invaded Iraq to overthrow Saddam Hussein. As a Brigadier General in the U.S. Army Reserves, Dr. Sienko commanded U.S. medical troops in both Kuwait and Iraq during the height of Operation Iraqi Freedom and continued to serve in the Iraq theatre for one year. Dr. Sienko is not a full-time soldier, however, but rather a dedicated public health officer. In his home state of Michigan, he has served since 1989 as the medical director and chief medical examiner of the Ingham County Health Department, based in Lansing. His training and experience in public health and preventive medicine have proven invaluable in his military life.

Dean Sienko was born in 1956 in Milwaukee, Wisconsin, and attended public schools in a working class, heavily Polish neighborhood on Milwaukee's South Side. After graduating from Pulaski High School in 1974, he enrolled at the University of Wisconsin Milwaukee, taking mostly liberal arts courses while completing prerequisite science courses to qualify for medical school. Medical school appealed to Dean because he viewed it as a means to help less-advantaged people. After graduation in 1978, he deferred his admission to the University of Wisconsin School of Medicine in Madison for one year, traveling overseas for seven months. His travels took him from North Africa to Sweden with stops throughout Western Europe and in East Berlin; for three months, he lived in Madrid to improve his Spanish.

During medical school, Dean joined the Wisconsin Army National Guard in recognition of his pride in America, a feeling shared by many in the immigrant neighborhood where he grew up. He spent one weekend per month and two weeks every summer on active duty, usually in a field hospital not far from Madison. Torn between specializing in psychiatry or preventive medicine, he traveled on his own after his third year to the Johns Hopkins University's School of Public Health to seek advice. Eager to learn more about preventive medicine, which received relatively little attention at his medical school, Dean met with a variety of public health experts to explore whether his interest in preventive medicine could be compatible with a medical career. Invigorated by the positive feedback he received, Dean took an elective course in epidemiology during his last year of medical school. The course was taught by Jeffrey Davis, the Wisconsin State Epidemiologist, and was such a positive experience that Dr. Davis recommended Dean for the Epidemic Intelligence Service (EIS) program at the Centers for Disease Control and Prevention (CDC) in Atlanta.

After a year at Cook County Hospital in Chicago on a rotating internship, Dean arrived at the CDC in July 1984 for his initial training as an EIS officer. He matched with the Michigan Department of Public Health in Lansing for a two-year stint and added a third year at the CDC in Atlanta to complete a residency in preventive medicine. Lansing was a fortuitous assignment – he was able to marry Mary Jean, a student in veterinary medicine at the University of Minnesota who transferred to Michigan State University in East Lansing to continue her studies. Trained as

a small animal veterinarian, Mary Jean Sienko focuses currently on the couple's three children, ages 8, 12 and 15, and has learned to adapt when Dean is on active duty.

During his two-year stint as an EIS officer assigned to the Michigan Department of Public Health, Dean traveled to Chad in Sub-Saharan Africa in 1985 to document the extent of a famine. The trip had been requested by the United States Agency for International Development (USAID) and his findings were published in the CDC's influential *Morbidity and Mortality Weekly Report*. In Michigan, Dean concentrated on communicable diseases and focused on acute disease epidemiology, dealing with salmonella, meningitis and measles outbreaks (a significant measles outbreak occurred in Ann Arbor in 1985). In 1987, he officially joined the Michigan Department of Public Health and dealt with chronic disease epidemiology and HIV/AIDS. A year and a half later, he became medical director and chief medical examiner of the Ingham County Health Department, where he has worked ever since.

Three times in his 22-year career Dean has been called up by the Reserves. After joining the Michigan Department of Public Health, he joined the Michigan Army National Guard. In 1991, he was called to Saudi Arabia during the Gulf War, serving from January until May on a Saudi Army base near Dhahran as a general medical officer. He and the hospital team treated hundreds of wounded Iraqi prisoners of war – he assisted orthopedic specialists with amputations and setting serious fractures – and the team also treated U.S. troops injured by an Iraqi SCUD attack on Dhahran.

In 2001, by now a full colonel, Dean was called up to serve in Kosovo as part of the ongoing peacekeeping mission. Based from March until October that year at Camp Bondsteel near Gjilane, he commanded a task force of 200 medical troops and helped oversee a merged medical facility for the U.S./U.K. combined command. He had daily exposure to international forces – British, French, German, Russian and Spanish – and welcomed the peacekeeping aspects of the job, a pleasant change from the tensions and horrors of war he had witnessed in Saudi Arabia.

In 2003, Dean was called up again to serve a year's tour of duty in the Iraq War. Now a Brigadier General, Dean arrived in Kuwait in March two days after U.S. and British forces began the invasion of Iraq. He commanded a force of 3,500 soldiers serving tens of thousands of troops and found that his background in public health had immediate benefits for the coalition forces. He instituted proactive, preventive approaches to three key health concerns in the Iraq theatre: mental health, heat and disease vectors. With daytime temperatures that can soar to 140 degrees in the Kuwaiti and Iraqi deserts, vital preventive approaches for both heat and mental health include cooled indoor environments, physical activity at night whenever feasible, and ready water sources at all times.

Still, mental health issues challenged Dean. The shocking incident of an enlisted man rolling a live grenade into a crowded tent, killing an officer and wounding many other soldiers, called for mental health providers to intervene immediately with witnesses, survivors and friends of the dead officer and injured soldiers. Another challenge, an increase in the number of suicides in July 2003, caused Dean to request assistance from a group of mental health experts from the Office of the Army Surgeon General. They flew to Kuwait and provided helpful advice about increasing mental health interventions for U.S. troops throughout the Middle East.

Dean and his team controlled the most worrisome disease vector, sand flies that cause leishmaniasis, through a combination of approaches. This unsightly condition, known as the Baghdad Boil, forms an ulcer on the skin. By stressing prevention (mosquito nets at night being an important preventive measure), health education and risk communication, Dean and his team of preventive medicine specialists contained the prevalence of leishmaniasis in Iraq. Troops moving through the An-Nasariyah area in South Central Iraq were at special risk due to the high prevalence of the disease in that area. Preventive measures included spraying safe levels of insecticide on the ground to contain sand flies, spraying military uniforms, and encouraging troops to apply DEET topically as an additional precaution.

Shortly after he arrived in Kuwait, Dean encountered cases of pneumonia among U.S. troops, some resulting in death. With his medical forces busy attending to their everyday activities, Dean called for assistance from the U.S. Army Center for Health Promotion and Preventive Medicine (USACHPPM), the Army Surgeon General, and the Walter Reed Army Institute of Research to help determine why pneumonia had become a problem. Teams of epidemiologists flew to Kuwait from the United States and investigated for 10 weeks. The anthrax vaccine that had been administered to all troops in the Iraq theatre was considered one possible cause, suspected for unanticipated side effects, perhaps in combination with other vaccines. Although the teams in the end could not agree on one underlying cause for the pneumonia cases, they did conclusively rule out the anthrax vaccine. Some investigators reported in their summary that

Working with Sharon Miller at Our Savior Lutheran Church Food Bank.

With Master Sergeant Michael A. Edgel.

With Major Bruce Bahr.

Quality time with his children, (l to r) Michael, Carolyn, and Peter.

Walking the base with Major Bruce Bahr.

recent tobacco use demonstrated some association with the pneumonia cases. As an epidemiologist, Dean appreciates the value of discovering the underlying causes of health problems; only then can preventive health specialists implement effective countermeasures and targeted education.

Just as Dean's background in public health and preventive medicine benefits the U.S. military, his work in the huge U.S. Army's Central Command will benefit the people of Ingham County. Based on his Iraq theatre experiences, he will organize and synchronize treatment approaches that meet the needs of the Ingham County population.

Dean Sienko still finds public health fascinating as an evolving science that integrates medicine with political and social science. It appeals to a person who seeks broad connection with social issues and approaches those issues with passion. A public health professional works on issues that deeply affect the well-being of others and at the same time reflect on the best values of society. For example, Dr. Sienko finds deep satisfaction, both professionally and personally, in providing health care for the uninsured, a key aspect of his work at the Ingham County Health Department.

Dean believes public health will gain even more relevance in the next 10 years. Although concern about bioterrorism was not predicted, it is here to stay. He predicts that food safety issues are likely to come under greater scrutiny due to the worldwide sources of the food supply.

At the Ingham County Health Department, Dean is involved in every aspect of running a local health department. With 350 employees, the department operates both a pediatric and an adult clinic and oversees progressive oral health programs, relying heavily on a well-trained staff of nurses, hygienists, nurse practitioners, dentists and physicians. With only five physicians on staff, the department frequently contracts for services of both physicians and dentists. Dean wakes up every morning raring to get to work. He loves the work he and his colleagues do that affects the lives of people so profoundly.

In giving back to his local community through the Ingham County Health Department, and to his country through the Army Reserves, Dr. Dean Sienko represents the best of public health in the United States.

Ardell Wilson, DDS, MPH

Connecticut

Creating a national model for asthma management

When *The New York Times* reported in May 2003 that one in four school-age children in central Harlem had asthma, even longtime asthma researchers were surprised. This New York City neighborhood had one of the highest rates of asthma ever documented in the United States. High rates of asthma are not limited to inner-city neighborhoods like Harlem, however. Dr. Ardell A. Wilson, chief of the Bureau of Community Health at the Connecticut Department of Public Health, knows this all too well. Born and raised in New York City – and living with asthma herself – Ardell confronted the disease and made Connecticut the first state in the nation to standardize the treatment protocol for asthma for school-age children.

A graduate of Washington Irving High School in Manhattan, Ardell enrolled at Bronx Community College to earn her associate degree. While still at Washington Irving, Ardell's guidance counselor pushed her to take college prep courses in advanced biology and advanced algebra even though she intended, like her elder sister, to stick with secretarial studies. That encouragement helped her do well at Bronx Community College. After graduating, and by this time married with a young son, she attended City College of the City University of New York part time, earning her bachelor's degree in 1976. She planned to major in elementary education but after one semester switched to biology, which she found more interesting.

As she completed her degree at City College, Ardell knew she wanted to work in health care. She chose dentistry because she felt it was the most stable health-related field – with a young son at home, she needed her work hours to be predictable. Ardell attended the Columbia University School of Dental and Oral Surgery for four years with the idea that she would start her own dental practice. During the last two years, she enlisted with the United States Public Health Service. In return for help with her tuition costs, she committed to practice in underserved areas for three years after graduation.

Upon graduation, Ardell joined the Boriken Neighborhood Health Center, a community health center in East Harlem, and spent three years there in an all-female dental service. She also worked at Columbia one day a week teaching preventive dentistry. Ardell believed that the preventive aspects of dentistry were more critical to a population's long-term health than corrective dentistry. During her final year at Boriken, and based on positive feedback from her preventive dentistry students, Columbia recruited Ardell to join the Division of Community Health as a faculty member. She taught ethics, jurisprudence and statistics and, at the same time, began a private practice in lower Manhattan, working there part time with a colleague from Columbia. Her work at Columbia was fulfilling because she could make an impact teaching those who in turn would serve the underserved. She also discovered in her private practice that she preferred the community health center setting, where she served those who were truly in need.

In 1984, the Robert Wood Johnson (RWJ) Health Services Research Scholars Program awarded Ardell a fellowship to study at Harvard. The program was intended to train academics to become leaders in health services research.

e Possible
MANAGE ASTHMA
Asthma Action Plan
= Keep pets outdoors,
carpets and stuffed toys;
of the bedroom.
= Eliminate "dust catchers"
= Fix all leaky
= Do not smoke
try to quit smoking
Make Your Home A Healthy Home
Prevent LEAD poisoning.

Dr. Howard Bailit, then at the Columbia University School of Public Health and now at the University of Connecticut, encouraged Ardell to apply for the RWJ program to broaden her perspective on health care delivery systems. At Harvard she worked with mentors outside of dentistry and was especially grateful for the training she received from Dr. Laurence Branch, a specialist in geriatrics, survey research and aging. During her fellowship, Ardell earned her master's degree in public health (MPH) from the Harvard School of Public Health with a concentration in maternal child health and aging. Although she lived apart from her family for two years – her husband and son remained in New Rochelle and they saw each other only on weekends – she would gladly choose to do those two years over again. She credits her experience at Harvard for preparing her to do what she does today.

At Harvard Ardell geared her research activities toward becoming a diplomate (specialist) of the American Board of Dental Public Health (ABDPH). She involved herself in learning everything she could about the aging of America, including health insurance and the delivery of services. She received a certificate in geriatrics from the Harvard School of Medicine Geriatric Education Center. With her mentor, Dr. Laurence Branch, she turned her attention to the most vulnerable elderly population, those living in nursing homes. Her work in this area resulted in the documentation of the oral health problems of the elderly living in nursing homes in Massachusetts and earned her the James M. Dunning Award in Health Services Research. She also became the first African-American woman diplomate of the ABDPH.

Upon completing her fellowship in 1986, Ardell returned to Columbia to direct the Division of Community Health and the joint degree program in public health and dentistry. In 1988 Connecticut recruited her to become the state's oral health director.

Ardell rose through a series of positions in Connecticut as the state restructured its government agencies numerous times. She served as the state's oral health director for only two months and then combined that position with community health programs involving school-based health centers, community health centers, maternal child health and substance abuse. In 1991, she became deputy director of the Connecticut Drug and Alcohol Abuse Commission. She oversaw four state hospitals serving substance abusers and collaborated with community-based agencies. Her greatest contribution, she believes, was expanding services for women by creating residential facilities where the women's children could join them.

In 1993, the Alcohol and Drug Abuse Commission merged into the newly named Connecticut Department of Public Health and Addiction Services, and Ardell reassumed some of her previous responsibilities in community health. In 1995, she became bureau chief of Community Health within a reconstituted Department of Public Health, a position she still holds. She supervises 150 to 200 people in a wide range of public health endeavors, including epidemiology, infectious disease, chronic disease, family health and risk assessment for environmental and occupational health. She also oversees the State Loan Repayment Program, which encourages young health professionals (physicians, dentists, hygienists, nurses) to practice in underserved areas while the state repays their school loans. Ardell also develops relationships with funders, mostly at the federal level, a key responsibility of her position.

In 2000, Ardell turned her attention to the issue of asthma, a chronic respiratory disease that affects an estimated 10.4 percent of Connecticut's children under age 18, or more than 86,000 children statewide. She collaborated with the New England regional task force on asthma as well as stakeholders from Connecticut – managed care organizations, community organizations and public health professionals – on a Pediatric Asthma Management Initiative. Those collaborations resulted in a model Asthma Action Plan for Connecticut. The Asthma Action Plan, a color-coordinated management tool, is developed in conjunction with a health care provider to help people manage asthma by teaching them to recognize when they are in the green zone (under control), yellow zone (need to improve control) or red zone (need immediate care). The Asthma Action Plan is available in both English and Spanish. Copies were distributed to clinical practices and managed care organizations throughout the state.

In 2001, on the heels of the Asthma Action Plan, Ardell convened a statewide Asthma Summit to publicize the extent of the asthma problem documented in the newly released "Asthma in Connecticut Report." The summit led to a Statewide Asthma Task Force charged with developing a Comprehensive Statewide Asthma Plan and Implementation Process. Numerous activities were initiated to address asthma – from public education and awareness campaigns and provider education to clinical management and surveillance activities. Because children spend a significant part of their day in school and school-related activities, a tool kit called "Managing Asthma in Schools" for school nurses (and school administrators) was developed with the help of school nurses. Shortly after, the Department of Public

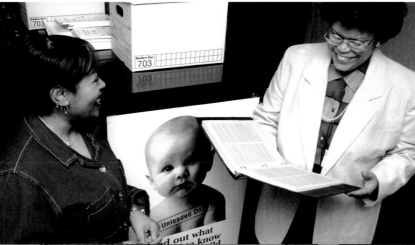

With administrative assistant, Blanche Mink.

At Hartford City Hall announcing a collaboration with *Aetna* with Dr. Ramon Rojano, director of Health & Human Services, City of Hartford.

Consulting with Dr. Robert Galvin, commissioner of public health for Connecticut.

Health helped day care providers develop their own kit called "Managing Asthma in Childcare Facilities." The tool kits – three-ring binders with inserts that can be reproduced as needed – addressed the facts of asthma triggers, asthma management and the administration of medications in simple and accessible terms. While the approach and materials were low-tech, they worked.

In 2003, the Connecticut legislature responded to the advocacy efforts of Ardell and the task force and passed legislation that gave the Department of Public Health the ability to collect data from schools and implement a statewide surveillance system for school children with asthma. This added to the department's ongoing hospital inpatient and outpatient surveillance activities. As someone with asthma herself, Ardell found the calendar sent by her managed care organization, based on the Asthma Action Plan materials, to be proof of the success of this initiative. The red, yellow and green indicators for the severity of an attack, matched to recommended interventions, are quick and handy references for anyone suffering from asthma.

The Association of State and Territorial Health Officials recognized Connecticut's Asthma Action Plan as a program of vision, the first of its kind in the nation and still leading the way. In addition to schools, Connecticut authorized day care personnel to administer medicine to treat asthma attacks as they occur, the first state to do so, making possible a continuum of care. The Connecticut Asthma Program distributes easy-to-use, understandable materials to all levels of the public health system – parents, school nurses, day care providers, physicians, clinics and hospitals. In fact, the department produced 10 educational pediatric asthma management

vignettes (with an interactive Web site) entitled "Natalie Says" directed at young children and their parents. The vignettes (in English and Spanish) review the importance of asthma management in a child-friendly way. The comprehensive array of asthma materials standardize asthma management protocol and help patients and caregivers understand what makes asthma worse and how to adjust medications and physical activities accordingly. The materials lead to effective management of asthma in children and are a testament to Ardell Wilson's vision and leadership.

Ardell believes this is an excellent time for young people to go into public health. For the first time, the human genome project offers hope that the genetic causes of some diseases can be discovered and the course of those diseases altered. The issue of health care access has come under greater scrutiny, with work force studies and evaluations of the fairness of insurance and delivery systems. Environmental health will continue to be at the center of public health, encouraging people to consider what they can do to make home and work environments safer. Yet another issue, public health systems that are needed to address health emergencies, has emerged front and center in the public eye.

Ardell believes that public health will be very different 10 years from now. Technologies now being perfected will make computer/Internet-based training the preferred method, replacing conferencing. A focus on the elderly population will be more pronounced, and research should advance treatment for Alzheimer's disease, falls and other perils of old age. The growing elderly population will require big increases in health care delivery systems, especially nursing homes and assisted living facilities. Ardell sees a bright

future for prevention and health promotion once education strategies that limit the growth of health care costs are recognized to work.

For Ardell Wilson, the journey from New York to Connecticut has been long but enjoyable. Along the way, she has made her mark as a dentist and public health specialist. Perhaps most significantly, she has been a literal breath of fresh air for the children and families of Connecticut. Her leadership in asthma management is a model for communities throughout the United States.

Epilogue

An important message that lies at the heart of *The Faces of Public Health* is the interconnectedness of our public health system. The infrastructure of the United States system comprises many layers and many committed professionals working in partnership to protect the population from disease and injury. Every layer and every individual touches our lives in different ways, many invisible to us.

In exploring the life stories of 25 people in the public health system, *The Faces of Public Health* focuses on people who represent many, but by no means all, layers of the system. The book portrays the daily work of people in the trenches, making a difference in their communities. These people work in state, city and county health departments and in other branches of government, as well as in clinics, hospitals and nonprofit organizations. None could succeed in their work without the training, funding, and support of many of our national, state and local institutions, philanthropies and governments, including the federal government's Centers for Disease Control and Prevention and National Institutes of Health.

Each person profiled in *The Faces of Public Health* gives personal advice to those who are considering careers in public health. We also asked them to project 10 years into the future, predicting where public health might be or where they hope it will go. They are optimistic that the American public will demonstrate a growing appreciation of public health and that, if resources can be properly aligned, a golden age may be in store for the field.

Each person profiled in this book protects and promotes the public's health in a specific way, yet they fall into five general public health missions – health promotion, advocacy, protection from illness, disease investigation and surveillance, and access to care. The groupings below reflect the major contribution each person has made to the public health system and to his or her community.

Health Promotion

Paul Juarez of California, *Dennis Murray* of Ohio, *Ron Graves* of Oklahoma, *Ardell Wilson* of Connecticut, *Janet Realini* of Texas and *Ellen Phillips-Angeles* of Washington state represent the front line of healthier communities.

 Paul, an academic, was a catalyst in applying public health techniques to the prevention and treatment of youth violence in Greater Los Angeles and helped to organize two mutually supportive nonprofit groups that work closely with law enforcement to end the cycle of youth violence.

 Dennis, a county health commissioner, proposed that a team of experts proactively address the issue of overweight and obesity in men; his research project focused on the most effective ways to educate physicians who, in turn, could educate their male patients about their lifestyle risks.

 Ron, a maxillofacial surgeon who, late in his career, was asked to serve on the Oklahoma Board of Health, collaborated with his governor, his state legislature, and with thought leaders throughout his state to effect smokeless indoor environments, a goal even the restaurant association in his state has come to applaud.

 Ardell, a dentist by training who runs the family and community health unit of her state's health department, formed teams to address asthma in young children. Living with asthma herself, Ardell implemented new treatment protocols that became a model for every state.

 Jan, an academic in family medicine who turned to public health later in her career, tackled the problem of unacceptably high rates of teen pregnancy in San Antonio and mobilized her community through an educational campaign to change teen behavior.

 Ellen, a health educator and champion of women's health, became the leader of a team in Seattle that makes early detection and treatment of breast and cervical cancer possible for uninsured, low-income women.

The great variety of approaches and the spectrum of action agencies are living reminders of the diversity of the field … public health is truly everywhere.

Advocacy

Chris Hoke of North Carolina, Kathleen Falk of Wisconsin and Marilyn Adams of Iowa are catalysts for change to ensure safer and healthier communities.

 Chris, a deputy director of his state's health department, works with his governor and state legislature to be sure that public health laws are up to date and can effectively address any emerging health threats.

 Kathleen, for years the public intervenor in the Wisconsin Department of Justice, was elected county executive in Dane County and pulled her citizens together to ensure careful land-use planning, a key to the environmental health of her county and to promoting healthy lifestyles for her growing population.

 Marilyn, a lifelong member of family farms, turned a personal tragedy into positive change for other farm families. Her growing nonprofit organization, Farm Safety 4 Just Kids, works with Congress, corporations and schools to educate children and adults about farm safety.

These faces show courage in conviction, strength in advocacy and commitment to the spectrum of partnerships needed for a successful public health system.

Protection From Illness

Debbie McCune Davis of Arizona, Aggie Leitheiser of Minnesota and Jean Malecki of Florida address emerging threats head-on to ensure the public's health.

 Debbie, a state legislator who is the program director of a statewide partnership for immunization, works across every level of the health care system in her state to promote a vaccine registry and boost the immunization rates for children.

 Aggie, deputy commissioner in her state's health department, oversaw Minnesota's response to preparedness following the events of September 11, 2001, involving citizens throughout her state and decentralizing the response structure to be sure all corners of her state could be protected if biological or chemical terrorism occurs.

 As the long-serving health director in Palm Beach County, Jean faced the country's first bioterrorist incident post-9/11, and calmly and authoritatively protected workers at the contaminated site, holding the fatalities from inhalation anthrax to one person.

These faces look outside their immediate communities, as well as inside, to ensure that all of the resources needed for public health can and will work together.

Disease Investigation and Surveillance

Marci Layton of New York, Denise Rondeau of New Hampshire, Elizabeth Laposata of Rhode Island and Garland Land of Missouri might be more correctly called public health detectives.

 Marci, the head of the disease investigation unit in the New York City Department of Health, contained an outbreak of the West Nile virus – the first verified in this country – by relying on old-fashioned footwork and some luck. She has since fully prepared her unit with syndromic surveillance systems that will identify potential outbreaks before they take hold.

 As an experienced HIV/AIDS and STD investigator, Denise's tireless work limited a syphilis outbreak that threatened to become an epidemic in her state through immediate contact tracing and effective counseling.

 Elizabeth, chief medical examiner for her state, applies the information from post-mortem exams to the protection functions of public health, resulting in earlier and clearer detection of environmental and communicable disease threats.

 Garland has been a visionary leader in innovating state-level data systems – automating data and getting it to flow in all directions as needed while protecting individual privacy, so that hospitals can continuously improve their quality and become centers of excellence.

These inquiring faces understand the basic rule that before you know where you are going, you need to know where you are. Basic to public health is the evidence base upon which its efforts must rest.

Ted Holloway of Georgia, *Amy Forsyth-Stephens* of Virginia, *Randy Lee* of Arkansas, *Jane Conard* of Alaska, *A. Cornelius Baker* of Washington, D.C., *Monserrate Salichs* of Puerto Rico, *Lisa Penny* of Idaho, *Russell Moy* of Maryland and *Dean Sienko* of Michigan bring health care to those in greatest need of it, whether due to cost or geographic obstacles.

 In his role as district health director for southeast Georgia, *Ted* finds ways to fund innovative health care approaches in a rural, generally poor corner of his state.

 Amy, a social worker by training, offers unparalleled pro bono access to mental health services for low-income, uninsured people in a rural corner of her state.

 Randy, a nurse, puts children first by engaging his community to eliminate disparities in health care for low-income, uninsured, under-insured and ethnic minority children.

 Jane brings primary care services to hard-to-reach Alaskans through an innovative itinerant nurse program.

 Cornelius and *Monserrate* direct clinics that reach underserved popula- tions with vital health services; each refuses to let ongoing funding problems affect the quality of care their clinics offer. Rather than curtailing services, each clinic director finds ways to continue serving people who are truly in need of health care.

 Lisa, a dental hygienist who directs oral health programs in her state's health department, brings healthy smiles to thousands of school children throughout Idaho, a state with a chronic shortage of dentists.

 Russell gave up a hands-on career in obstetrics to become a hands-on public health practitioner in his state's health department, improving systems for maternal and child health.

 As the medical director of his county's health department and a former Epidemic Intelligence Service officer, *Dean* put his public health skills to work to improve conditions for U.S. troops serving in Kuwait and Iraq during his tour of duty in the Iraq War as a Brigadier General in the Army Reserves.

These caring faces remind us that while public health is a combination of many different approaches and strategies, each member of the community provides personal services that complement broader efforts.

The future of public health lies not only in the hands of these exemplary public health practitioners but also in the hands of more than 400,000 public health workers who serve every community in our country and in the ideas of a generation yet to come. In profiling these 25 individuals, we are celebrating all public health workers who selflessly watch over our communities to ensure our health and safety. It is often said that when public health is done right, it is invisible. *The Faces of Public Health* reminds us that those who commit their lives to this unseen work have a face. We celebrate all the faces of public health and thank them for their contributions, large and small.

The Faces of Public Health
Honor Roll

The people listed below were nominated by their respective state or local health department for contributing to the public health of their communities. We honor these faces of public health.

Frederick Altice
Yale University School of Medicine
New Haven, Connecticut

Robert Bernstein
Texas Health Foundation
Austin, Texas

Catherine Bodenhamer
Baxter County Health Unit
Mt. Home, Arkansas

R. Scott Chavez
National Commission on
Correctional Health Care
Chicago, Illinois

Mark Converse
AAA Southern New England
Providence, Rhode Island

Claude Dharamaj
Pinellas County Health Department
St. Petersburg, Florida

Joan H. Ellison
Livingston County Department of Health
Mt. Morris, New York

Alison Ensminger
American Cancer Society Relay for Life
Seattle, Washington

Peter Fornal
Human Resource Consultants
East Greenwich, Rhode Island

Harold Freeman
Ralph Lauren Center for
Cancer Care and Prevention
New York, New York

Julie Gralow
University of Washington School of
Medicine/Seattle Cancer Care Alliance
Seattle, Washington

Elizabeth (Libby) Greene
South Carolina Department of
Health and Environmental Control
Columbia, South Carolina

Annie De Groot
Brown University
Providence, Rhode Island

Dirk Haselow
Arkansas Department of Health
Little Rock, Arkansas

Debra Henderson
Marion County Health Department
Indianapolis, Indiana

Jim Hyde
Tufts University School of Medicine
Boston, Massachusetts

Jeff Johnson
Beacon Mutual Insurance Company
Warwick, Rhode Island

Sandi Johnson
Evergreen Healthcare
Kirkland, Washington

Ken Kauffman
Oregon Department of Human Services
Salem, Oregon

Stanley Kondracki
New York State Department of Health
Albany, New York

Thomas Locke
Washington State Board of Health
Sequim, Washington

Patricia Lopez
Lincoln-Lancaster County
Health Department
Lincoln, Nebraska

Carol Maikainai
Life Foundation
Oahu, Hawaii

Gloria Maki
New York State Department
of Health AIDS Institute
Albany, New York

Mike May
Harborview Medical Center
Seattle, Washington

Joan Miles
Lewis & Clark City-County
Health Department
Helena, Montana

Michael Moomey
Illinois Department of Public Health
Springfield, Illinois

**Douglas Mormann and the La Crosse Area
Health Initiative**
La Crosse County Health Department
La Crosse, Wisconsin

Ralph Morris
Minnesota Department of Health
Bemidji, Minnesota

Richard Morrissey
Kansas Department of Health
and Environment
Topeka, Kansas

John C. Nelson
American Medical Association
Chicago, Illinois

Lloyd F. Novick
Onondaga County Department of Health
Syracuse, New York

Edna Poulin
Rhode Island Department of Health
Providence, Rhode Island

John Poundstone
Lexington-Fayette County
Health Department
Lexington, Kentucky

Deborah Prothrow-Stith
Harvard School of Public Health
Boston, Massachusetts

Sam Sanchez
San Antonio Metropolitan Health District
San Antonio, Texas

Margaret Schmelzer
Wisconsin Department of
Health & Family Services
Madison, Wisconsin

Julie Scofield
National Alliance of State and
Territorial AIDS Directors
Washington, D.C.

Judith Seltzer
Reno County Health Department
Hutchinson, Kansas

Jane Smith
Idaho Division of Health
Boise, Idaho

Jay Smith
Logan County Health Department
Guthrie, Oklahoma

Sandra Snow
Baxter County Health Unit
Little Rock, Arkansas

Liza Solomon
Maryland Department of Health
and Mental Hygiene
Baltimore, Maryland

Matthew Stefanak
Mahoning County General Health
District Board of Health
Youngstown, Ohio

Leslee Stein-Spencer
Illinois Department of Health
Springfield, Illinois

Gary Stevens
Jackson County Health Department
Medford, Oregon

Sara Reed Stinchcomb
Physicians' Campaign for a
Healthier Oklahoma
Edmond, Oklahoma

Richard Taffner
Baxter County Health Unit
Mt. Home, Arkansas

Jack Thompson
Northwest Center for Public Health Practice
Seattle, Washington

Lou Turner
State Laboratory of Public Health
Raleigh, North Carolina

Charles Weatherby
Primary Care Physician
Tacoma, Washington

James C. Welch
Delaware Division of Public Health
Dover, Delaware

Mary Wellik
Olmsted County Health Department
Rochester, Minnesota

Eric Whitehead
Florida Department of Health
Tallahassee, Florida

Pheamo Witcher
Genesis Center
Providence, Rhode Island

Warren Wollschlager
Connecticut Department of Health
Hartford, Connecticut

Betsy Wood
Florida Department of Health
Tallahassee, Florida

Lester Wright
New York State Department of
Correctional Services
Albany, New York